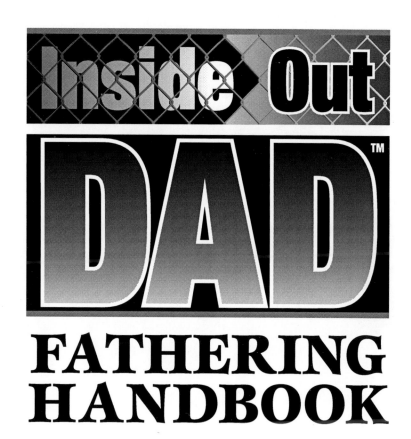

Inside Out

DAD™

FATHERING HANDBOOK

To Learn More About NFI and the InsideOut Dad™ Program:

TRAINING, TECHNICAL ASSISTANCE AND QUESTIONS ABOUT THE INSIDEOUT DAD™ PROGRAM

Phone: (301) 948-0599
Fax: (301) 948-4325
Email: corrections@fatherhood.org
Website: www.fatherhood.org

LEARN MORE ABOUT NATIONAL FATHERHOOD INITIATIVE

National Fatherhood Initiative®
www.fatherhood.org

101 Lake Forest Boulevard, Suite 360
Gaithersburg, MD 20877

Phone: (301) 948-0599
Fax: (301) 948-4325
Email: info@fatherhood.org
Website: www.fatherhood.org

First Edition
Christophe Beard, Christopher Brown, John Chacón, Steven Hane, Karen Patterson
With contributions from Stephen Bavolek, Ph.D., CEO & Founder of Family Development Resources, Inc.

© 2005 National Fatherhood Initiative   Printed in the United States of America.

ISBN 1-933560-08-8 / 978-1-933560-08-3   898-08-2008-NFI-CNA-47

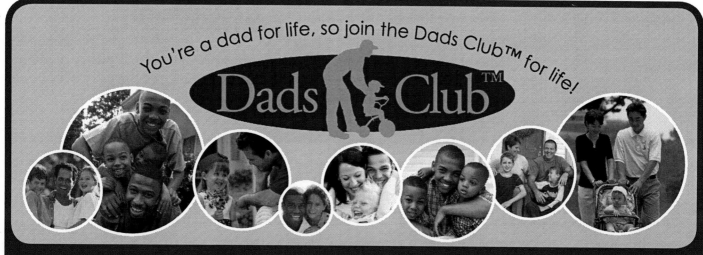

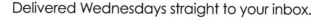

InsideOut Dad™

Fathering Handbook

TABLE OF CONTENTS

CORE Session 1.0
Setting the Rules and Completing the InsideOut Dad™ Survey

"The journey of a thousand miles begins with the first step."
—Lao-tzu, Chinese Philosopher
(604 BC - 531 BC)

In this session, your facilitator will introduce you to the InsideOut Dad™ program. Over the course of this program, you will learn how to be a more involved, responsible and committed father. You will create an action plan for putting this knowledge to work.

After each session, you will write down what you learned, how what you learned will help you to be a better dad, and one way you will be a better dad. This program is will help you be a better dad over time.

There are 12 core sessions in this program along with 26 optional sessions. Your facilitator will explain how many sessions you will have in your program.

Your facilitator will explain the rules for this program during this first session. Be sure to follow them all. They exist to help you get the most out of this program.

You will take a survey at the start of this program and again at the end of the program. Your facilitator will compare your answers on the survey that you gave at the start of the program to the answers you will give at the end of the program. Taking these surveys will help you know how much your knowledge of how to be a good dad grew during the program.

NOTES:

_____

_____

_____

_____

_____

_____

_____

_____

_____

_____

_____

_____

_____

_____

_____

_____

_____

Session Log
Setting the Rules and Completing the InsideOut Dad™ Survey

One new thing I learned today was_____

_____

_____

_____.

This information will help me become a better dad because_____

_____

_____

_____.

One way I will be a better dad is_____

_____

_____

_____.

Notes:

_____

_____

_____

_____

_____

OPTIONAL Session 1.1
Welcome; Hopes and Fears; Orientation

"There are two mistakes one can make along the road to truth: not going all the way, and not starting."
—Buddha (563 BC - 483 BC)

Getting started is always hard to do. Because you are taking this long journey, your first steps are very important. So, let's start at the beginning.

To me, parenting means _____

_____

_____

_____

_____ .

The parent I want to be is _____

_____

_____

_____

_____ .

What are some "hopes" that you have? _____

_____

_____

_____

_____

_____ .

What are some "fears" that you have? _____

_____

_____

_____

_____

_____ .

By attending parenting classes, I **hope** that

_____

_____

_____ , but I'm **afraid** that___

_____

_____ .

What does the word **trust** mean to you?

_____

_____

_____

_____

_____.

Here are some reasons why trust is important:

- Trust is the basis for all healthy relationships.

- Trust helps you be close to others.

- Trust gives a sense of hope and well-being.

- Trust is the first issue young children face in life that gives them their view of the world.

Session Log
Welcome; Hopes and Fears; Orientation

One new thing I learned today was_____

_____

_____

_____.

This information will help me become a better dad because_____

_____

_____

_____.

One way I will be a better dad is_____

_____

_____

_____.

Notes:

_____

_____

_____

_____

_____

_____

CORE Session 2.0
Remembering My Past

"We should not look back, unless it is to derive useful lessons from past errors…"
—George Washington (1732-1799)

The more a man knows about his qualities, both positive and negative, and his traits, both good and bad, the more control he has over his behavior.

About Me Inventory
Complete the statements below.

1. One of my earliest childhood memories of being a little boy is:

_____

_____

_____

_____

_____.

2. The influence my dad had on me was (circle one):

Positive   Negative   About 50-50

3. The influence my mother had on me was (circle one):

Positive   Negative   About 50-50

4. What I learned about relationships watching my mom and dad was (circle one):

a. Relationships between Dad and Mom / husband and wife can be loving.
b. Relationships between Dad and Mom / husband and wife can be unsupportive and hurting.
c. Children are a positive, not negative part of the Dad-Mom / husband-wife relationship.
d. Dads/Husbands are controlling and forceful.
e. Moms/Wives are controlling and forceful.
f. Other_____

_____

_____.

My Story, My Life

Use this page to write "My Story, My Life" in your own words. It is for you to keep and share with your children. You will need to show this story to your facilitator and will have the chance to share with the group if you like. You don't have to share your story if you don't want to.

This story is about _____ (Your Name).

My story begins in _____ (Place of Birth) in the year_____ (Date of Birth). In the beginning, I lived with _____

_____

_____.

(Write what you know or remember about your childhood family.)

I started school when I was ____ years old and lived in_____. My favorite memories of school are _____

_____

_____

_____.

Some of the things that bring back bad memories are _____

_____

_____.

The first time I got in trouble with the law was

_____

_____

_____

_____

_____.

Today, the major supports in my life are_____

_____

_____

_____.

(Current Family)

Really, this story is about a little boy who grows up believing _____ _____ _____ and then finds out that later in life that _____ _____ _____ _____.

In my life, there have been real heroes, people I looked up to in my life like_____ _____ _____. But there were other people that I did not look up to or respect because _____ _____ _____.

There have been and still are many challenges in life faced by this boy and man, that include _____ _____ _____, but the best memory takes place in _____ when _____ _____ _____ _____.

Today, I will begin to plan and write the script for the rest of my life. At the end of the story, the people who care about me will say _____ _____ _____ _____.

What makes this time so great is _____ _____.

Session Log
Remembering My Past

One new thing I learned today was_____

_____

_____

_____.

This information will help me become a better dad because_____

_____

_____

_____.

One way I will be a better dad is_____

_____

_____

_____.

Notes:

_____

_____

_____

_____

_____

_____

OPTIONAL Session 2.1
What Kind of Father Am I?

"Self-knowledge is the beginning of self-improvement."
—Baltasar Gracián, Spanish Philosopher and Writer (1601-1658)

Being a caring and loving father is linked to being a caring and loving man. The traits of who we are as men are the same traits we show in our family roles.

A nurturing man shows these traits as a dad. An uncaring man shows these traits as an uncaring father. The InsideOut Dad is a caring man in all aspects of his life.

Father Checklist
Place a Y (Yes), N (No) or S (Sometimes) on the line by the traits you feel best show the type of father you are. This checklist is designed so that you can check the traits whether or not you have been with your children. If you have lived with your children, rate yourself based on the kind of father you were to them. If you have never been with your children, rate yourself as you would be if you were with them.

Y = Yes, this is me.
N = No, this is not me.
S = Sometimes this is me.

1. I am/would be open to listening to my children's points of view. _____

2. I can/would negotiate and compromise with my children when it is good to do so. _____

3. I am/would be clearly in charge of my children. _____

4. I expect/would expect my children to follow the rules I set down. _____

5. I demand/would demand respect from my children. _____

6. I tell/would tell my children how I feel. _____

7. I am willing/would be willing to change my ideas about how to raise my children. _____

8. I show/would show my children that I feel close to them. _____

9. I like/would like being in control of my children. _____

10. I enjoy/would enjoy spending quality time with my children. _____

11. I am able/would be able to listen to the good as well as the bad from my children. _____

12. I am clearly seen/would clearly be seen as a friend to my children. _____

13. My children can come/could come to me to talk. _____

14. I am a caring/would be a caring and giving father. _____

15. I easily/would easily have fun with my children. _____

Session Log
What Kind of Father Am I?

One new thing I learned today was_____

_____

_____

_____.

This information will help me become a better dad because_____

_____

_____

_____.

One way I will be a better dad is_____

_____

_____

_____.

Notes:

_____

_____

_____

_____

_____

_____

CORE Session 3.0

What is a Man?

"A man is what he wills himself to be."
—Jean-Paul Sartre (1905-1980)

"The essence of man is not in what he is, but in what he is able to be."
—Abraham Heschel (1907-1972)

To me, masculinity (what it means to be a

man) means_____

_____

_____

_____.

The trait of masculinity I most admire is_____

_____

_____

_____

_____.

The trait of masculinity I least admire is_____

_____

_____

_____

_____.

The Meanings of Masculinity

The concept of "masculinity" (what it means to be a man) is learned from culture and family.

In the 1980s, researchers identified a list of traits that people used to describe masculinity. These traits are listed in the table below.

Has that list of traits changed today? Rate yourself on each of the seven traits from the 1980s and the traits of Today using the 0 to 3 scale below.

0   Not at all
1   Little
2   Average
3   A lot

Trait	1980s	Today
Self-confident		
Courageous		
Leadership		
Dependable		
Successful		
Self-reliant		
Controlling (situations or other people)		

List the traits that describe masculinity today and rate yourself on those.

What traits would you like to pass on to your sons?_____

_____

_____

_____.

What would you want to teach your daughters about relationships with men by modeling certain traits?_____

_____

_____

_____.

Session Log
What Is A Man?

One new thing I learned today was_____

_____

_____

_____.

This information will help me become a better dad because_____

_____

_____

_____.

One way I will be a better dad is_____

_____

_____

_____.

Notes:

_____

_____

_____

_____

_____

_____

OPTIONAL Session 3.1

Masculinity and the Media

All our lives, we have seen images about what it means to be a "real man." The media, through TV, radio and print, sends images of what it means to be a man. Do these images show what it means to be a real man?

How does the media show what it means to be a man for a…

a. Male Movie Actor

_____

b. Playboy

_____

c. NASCAR Driver

_____

d. Football Player

_____

e. Business CEO

_____

f. Politician

_____

g. Rock Musician

_____

h. Rapper

_____

i. Drill Sergeant

_____

j. Father

_____

k. Sports Announcer

_____

l. TV Actor playing lawyer, doctor, law enforcement officer

_____

m. Comedian

_____

n. Auto Assembly Line Worker

_____

o. Male Clergy Member (priest, pastor, rabbi, etc.)

_____

Session Log
Masculinity and the Media

One new thing I learned today was_____

_____

_____

_____.

This information will help me become a better dad because_____

_____

_____

_____.

One way I will be a better dad is_____

_____

_____

_____.

Notes:

_____

_____

_____

_____

_____

_____

OPTIONAL Session 3.2
Physical and Mental Health

"Health is better than wealth."
—An English proverb

"Take care of your body. It's the only place you have to live."
—Jim Rohn, Successful Author and Businessman

Part 1
Men don't like to go to the doctor because_____

_____

_____

_____.

When was the last time you saw a doctor?

_____.

Why did you go?

_____.

Should the reasons why men don't go to the doctor keep you from going, too?

_____

_____

_____.

Part 2
Answer the following statements:

Right now, the part of my physical or mental health that I am most concerned about is

_____

_____

_____.

Right now, I need to_____

_____

_____to take

better care of my physical and mental health.

One thing I can do to improve my physical

health is_____

_____

_____.

One thing I can do to improve my mental

health is_____

_____

_____.

If your children wanted to write you a brief letter asking you to take better care of your health, what would it say?

Would they talk about wanting you to come to see them graduate from high school? Or maybe the letter would be about you staying healthy so you can see them get married and have kids one day?

Pretend to be your child (or one of your children) and write out this letter.

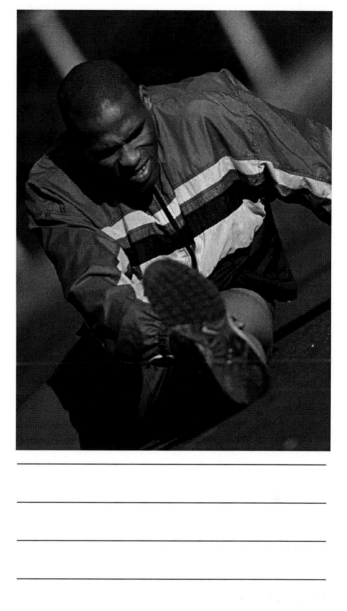

_____

_____

_____

_____

_____

_____

_____

_____

_____

_____

_____

_____

_____

_____

_____

_____

_____

_____

Session Log
Physical and Mental Health

One new thing I learned today was_____

_____

_____

_____.

This information will help me become a better dad because_____

_____

_____

_____.

One way I will be a better dad is_____

_____

_____

_____.

Notes:

_____

_____

_____

_____

_____

_____

CORE Session 4.0
Spirituality and Family

"Great men are they who see that spiritual is stronger than any material force."
—Ralph Waldo Emerson

What does Emerson mean by his statement?

_____

_____.

The word "spirituality" has to do with the spirit of the soul:

- It is our moral, religious or emotional nature as humans.
- It is the part of each person that feels a great tie to, or part of someone or something else.
- It is a feeling of being a member of or belonging to a cause or organization.
- It is the force of life that tries to find meaning and purpose.

Spirituality is love, it is kindness, it is caring and it is also faith.

To me, spirituality means _____

_____,

and religion means _____

_____.

Spirituality is a part of who we are – just like our arms, legs, and heads. Religion is a set of rituals, and traditions that reflect certain beliefs about the universe, our place in it and how we are linked to a higher power. Many men use religion to show their spirituality. Both can exist together and apart from one another.

Can you think of some examples of how people might show their spirituality?

1. _____

_____.

2. _____

_____.

3. _____

_____.

Two ways I have shown my spirituality as a man are _____
and _____.

Two ways I have shown my spirituality as a father are _____
and _____.

A "spiritual family" is one that feels a bond between all its members and where the members feel that they belong. When "family spirituality" is present, members cooperate, love and respect each other and communicate well.

Family Spirituality Checklist

Please use the rating scale below to respond to the statements about you and your family.

1 Not at all
2 Sometimes
3 Always

	Before Incarceration (Past)	During Incarceration (Present)	After Release (Future, If You Will Be or Plan To Be Released)
1. My family members pray or meditate regularly.			
2. We tell our family members and others to maintain a spiritual lifestyle.			
3. We show love and affection for each other.			
4. We attend spiritual activities together (church, temple, mosque, discussion groups, etc.).			
5. We are aware of how our actions affect other people.			
6. Family members tolerate and forgive each another.			
7. Our family members talk about spiritual issues with each other.			
8. Our adult family members teach our children about spirituality.			
9. We rely on our spirituality to help us through the hard times.			
10. Our spirituality affects the choices we make every day about how we treat family members and others.			

One thing I can do right away to build our family spirituality is:_____

_____.

Session Log
Spirituality and Family

One new thing I learned today was_____

_____

_____

_____.

This information will help me become a better dad because_____

_____

_____

_____.

One way I will be a better dad is_____

_____

_____

_____.

Notes:

_____

_____

_____

_____

_____

_____

Spirituality and Change

"You must be the change you wish to see in the world."
—Gandhi (1869-1948)

The InsideOut Dad thinks about his thoughts, feelings and actions every day to make sure that he respects himself, others and his environment. When the InsideOut Dad realizes that he has disrespected someone, he apologizes and is careful not to do so again. For the InsideOut Dad to do this, he must be "open for change."

Postures towards Acceptance of Change

"Fight or Flight"
This is the posture of defense and attack. When someone suggests change, the person gets into a "fight or flight" mindset.

Some examples of a "Fight or Flight" posture are when someone blames, becomes angry, ignores the need for change, criticizes, starts a fight or leaves the scene.

Here is an example of criticizing:

Fred's Wife: "You know Fred, you're never around at night to help put the kids to sleep. I really need your help."

Fred: "Well, if you were more organized, you wouldn't need my help. The problem with you is ..."

"Defensive/Closed"
This is the posture of the child. When someone suggests change, the person closes up. Some examples of a "Defensive/Closed" posture are when someone withdraws, becomes stubborn or silent, denies the need for change or makes excuses.

Here is an example of denial:

Fred's Wife: "You know Fred, you're never around at night to help put the kids to sleep. I really need your help."

Fred: "I don't remember you ever asking me for help. Am I a mind reader?"

"Open for Change"
This is the posture of the InsideOut Dad. When someone suggests change, the InsideOut Dad listens to the need for change. Some examples of an "Open for Change" posture are when someone makes eye contact (in some cultures, but not in others), looks interested, has a pleasant tone, asks questions, wants to help and seeks to clarify the need for change.

Here is an example of a desire to help:

Fred's Wife: "You know Fred, you're never around at night to help put the kids to sleep. I really need your help."

Fred: "I'm sorry. I haven't been there to help you. Let's make a plan. What can we do to work together?"

The most important factors in helping you to be "open to change" are:

- <u>Valuing the need to change.</u> The changes need to have worth before you can make a sincere effort to change.

- <u>Valuing the other person</u>. If someone you don't respect tells you that you need to change, his or her comments will seem more like nagging.

- <u>Being mindful</u>. Be aware of your thoughts and feelings, how you come across to the other person, the mood of the person you are talking with, the situation, etc. This awareness is vital for using the best judgment in responding.

- <u>Having the right skills and the "know how" to change is an art and a science</u>. Knowing how to change will help create the change.

Session Log
Spirituality and Change

One new thing I learned today was_____

_____

_____

_____.

This information will help me become a better dad because_____

_____

_____

_____.

One way I will be a better dad is_____

_____

_____

_____.

Notes:

_____

_____

_____

_____

_____

OPTIONAL Session 4.2
Ways to Increase Spirituality

"Be prepared spiritually for things that will interrupt your spirituality . . . at home, at work, at church meetings . . . in any situation."
—Unknown

To me, spirituality means _____

_____

_____

_____.

One way men differ from women spiritually is

_____

_____

_____.

One way men and women are alike spiritually is

_____

_____

_____.

Spirituality is a feeling of membership or belonging, force of life, feeling of a tie to something else of a moral, religious or emotional nature, or part of something or someone else. Think of love, kindness, caring, faith.

Ways to Build Spirituality

<u>Take time for yourself</u>. It is important to take time during the day and week to do things that lead to your good health.

<u>Keep a journal</u>. Write down thoughts and feelings a few times a month about the events in your life. It's neat to look back and see how you've changed.

<u>Exercise</u>. A healthy body often leads to a healthy sense of spirituality.

<u>Read</u>. Increase your imagination, knowledge and creativity.

<u>Meditate or Pray</u>. Relax your mind by taking the time to think about that which is great and good.

<u>Be positive</u>. Communication has a ripple effect. Be positive and create positive ripples.

<u>Eat and sleep well</u>. The body needs to be cared for. Keep it healthy.

<u>Develop good relationships</u>. Choose to be with people who have a good affect on you. Develop relationships with other men and fathers who support your spirituality and your desire to be an InsideOut Dad.

<u>Support a cause</u>. Rally around a cause and make the world a better place to live in.

<u>Volunteer</u>. Give your time and energy to help others.

Session Log
Ways to Increase Spirituality

One new thing I learned today was_____

_____

_____

_____.

This information will help me become a better dad because_____

_____

_____

_____.

One way I will be a better dad is_____

_____

_____

_____.

Notes:

_____

_____

_____

_____

_____

_____

CORE Session 5.0

Expressing Anger in Males and Females

"Bad things do happen; It's how I respond to them that defines my character and the quality of my life…"
—Walter Anderson, American Artist and Author

To me, the feeling of anger is _____

_____

_____

_____.

(Describe the feeling of anger.)

When I get angry, it's usually because_____

_____

_____

_____.

Anger is a secondary emotion that often comes from past pain or hurt that is not dealt with. When people become angry, they are often showing past hurt or pain.

Examples:

Your friend says something hurtful to you, but you say nothing. The next time you see him, you want to fight him because of what he said.

What happened?

Your boss criticizes your work. You think he is being unfair, but don't want to tell him that. You come home and yell at the children for not doing their homework.

What happened?

Your in-law or neighbor has been putting down the way you parent for years. You feel hurt, but don't say anything and just grin and bear it. One day he makes a harmless comment or joke and you explode.

What happened?

Think about a few times when you've gotten angry. How did you handle your anger then? How do you handle your anger these days? In the same way? In a different way?

Some Facts and Myths about Anger

1. Men often find it harder to show their feelings of hurt than women.
<u>Fact</u>. Men often find it harder to show all feelings compared to women and children.

2. Boy babies are fussier, easer to excite, harder to calm down and respond to change with less ease than girl babies.
<u>Fact</u>. Boy babies tend to be fussier, get more excited, are harder to calm down and respond to change with less ease than girl babies. As a result, boys are "hushed" to be quieter.

3. Boys are taught not to cry; girls are taught it is okay to cry.
<u>Fact</u>. Boys are taught to keep their tears inside. To cry might be seen as a sign of weakness and a loss of masculinity.

4. When boys show their anger, they tend to be more violent than girls.
<u>Fact</u>. Males tend to commit more violent crimes than females. Anger is the emotion that most often leads males to be violent.

- Boys are taught to show their angry energy in aggressive ways, often by hitting something.

- Boys are also taught to get angry and to take their anger out on their enemy in contact sports, such as boxing, wrestling, football and hockey. The result is a high number of fights in male sporting events.

- Many girls, on the other hand, are taught not to show their anger at all. This creates lots of stress that could be related to girls becoming anxious and depressed.

There are four goals in managing anger:

1. Be aware of feelings of hurt when they happen and show them in proper ways at all times. When you bury hurtful feelings or deny them, it only builds up anger energy inside.

2. Be aware of feelings of anger when they happen so that you can show your anger calmly.

3. Show the anger energy in proper ways. Don't hit, yell, call someone bad names or abuse someone in any other way.

4. Teach your children how to express their anger in proper ways by being a good role model.

Session Log
Expressing Anger in Males and Females

One new thing I learned today was_____

_____

_____

_____.

This information will help me become a better dad because_____

_____

_____

_____.

One way I will be a better dad is_____

_____

_____

_____.

Notes:

_____

_____

_____

_____

_____

_____

OPTIONAL Session 5.1
Stress and Anger

"Those who are at war with others are seldom at peace with themselves."
—Unknown

What does the term "mental health" mean to you?

_____

_____

_____.

There is a link between mental health and physical health—each one affects the other.

A good example of the link is the body's response to the feeling of anger.

It's called **stress**!

Stressors are the triggers in life that cause or add to stressful times. Although you can't control some stressors, you can control the way you handle your stress.

Ways to Reduce Stress
1. Regular exercise
2. Proper diet
3. Regular and enough sleep
4. Psychological/marital/spiritual counseling
5. Change jobs or careers
6. Cutback on spending; seek to reduce debt
7. Other ideas:

_____

_____.

Anger
Anger is often linked to stress. Anger is mostly a secondary emotion. It reveals past pain or hurt. When a person buries his feelings, it is like stepping on a spring. When the pressure is off, feelings spring out. Because all feelings and thoughts have energy, it is the way people release the energy that can get them into trouble.

As young boys, many men learned that by using fists to hit something (like a pillow) they could release anger. The sad thing is that the link between anger and violence has grown into a major social crisis: young boys and men showing their anger through violence.

One way I express my anger is _____

_____

_____.

I learned to express it in this way because ____

_____

_____.

One way my children express their anger is

_____

_____

_____.

They learned this way from_____

_____

_____.

How to Show Anger in A Proper Way

To show anger in a proper way; think about these rules:

1. **Respect yourself** - Don't hurt yourself.
2. **Respect others** - Don't hurt others.
3. **Respect the environment** - Don't disrespect your environment.

To express anger in proper ways:

Step 1: Find a way to release your anger energy in a proper way.

Step 2: Talk with someone about what happened.

Sometimes people need to do Step 2 before they do Step 1. The danger in doing Step 2 first is that the volume, tone and content of the message is so full of anger that the angry person uses hurting words.

You need to have a plan in place on proper ways to show your anger.

Session Log
Stress and Anger

One new thing I learned today was_____

_____

_____

_____.

This information will help me become a better dad because_____

_____

_____

_____.

One way I will be a better dad is_____

_____

_____

_____.

Notes:

_____

_____

_____

_____

_____

_____

OPTIONAL Session 5.2
Drinking and Stress

"About half of state prison inmates and 40 % of federal prisoners incarcerated for committing violent crimes report they were under the influence of alcohol or drugs at the time of their offense."
—U.S. Department of Justice Statistics, 1997

When I feel stressed, I usually resort to_____

_____

_____.

One way stress harms my health is_____

_____

_____.

Stress and Alcohol Quiz

Is the statement Myth or a Fact? Circle your answer:

1. **Drinking alcohol lowers your stress.**
   Myth   Fact
2. **Stress causes alcoholism.**
   Myth   Fact
3. **People don't know when they are addicted to alcohol.**
   Myth   Fact
4. **You can inherit alcoholism.**
   Myth   Fact
5. **Alcoholism can be cured.**
   Myth   Fact
6. **Women should not drink if they are pregnant.**
   Myth   Fact

Answers to Stress and Alcohol Quiz

1. Drinking alcohol lowers your stress.
Myth and Fact. Alcohol in small amounts might lessen the body's response to stress. Studies show, however, that alcohol raises stress by causing the body to produce the same hormones the body produces under stress.

2. Stress causes alcoholism.
Myth. Stress does not cause alcoholism, but problem drinking is often linked to stress.

3. People don't know when they are addicted to alcohol.
Myth. There are symptoms that clearly show problem drinking. Two common symptoms are lots of drinking after an fight with your wife/partner, when your boss gives you a hard time or when you feel under pressure.

4. You can inherit alcoholism.
Fact. Alcoholism runs in families. Genes the person inherits and lifestyle both play a role. But not all children of alcoholics become alcoholic. And some people can become alcoholics even though no one in their family has a drinking problem.

5. Alcoholism can be cured.
Myth. Alcoholism can't be cured at this time. Even if an alcoholic hasn't been drinking for a long time, he can suffer a relapse. To guard against a relapse, an alcoholic must avoid all drinks with alcohol.

6. Women should not drink if they are pregnant.
Fact. Fetal Alcohol Syndrome (FES) is mental retardation that is caused from drinking during pregnancy. Alcohol use lowers a man's sperm count, which can lead to problems in trying to have children.

Session Log
Drinking and Stress

One new thing I learned today was_____

_____

_____

_____.

This information will help me become a better dad because_____

_____

_____

_____.

One way I will be a better dad is_____

_____

_____

_____.

Notes:

_____

_____

_____

_____

_____

_____

www.fatherhood.org

OPTIONAL Session 5.3
Carrying Emotions

"Our best evidence of what people truly feel and believe comes less from their words than from their deeds."
—Robert Cialdin, American Professor of Psychology

One feeling I have difficulty handling is _____

_____.

When I feel _____,

I usually behave _____

_____

_____.

Feelings and thoughts have energy. The energy that comes with each feeling and thought wants to be released.

Every experience we have also comes with thoughts and feelings. Memories are the thoughts about experiences in our past. Whether these memories are good or bad depends on the experience. Good times give us good memories; bad or painful times leave us with bad memories.

A feeling is tied to every memory. We can label feelings as feelings of comfort or discomfort. Talking about feelings in this way takes away the notion of some feelings being "bad" and some being "good."

All feelings tell us something about an experience. Men are raised from an early age not to show feelings and to keep them inside. The result is the increase in physical and emotional problems men struggle with in their lives.

The more we cover up our feelings, the less freedom we have. The more experiences we cover up, the more energy it takes and the less growth we can make. Depression, stress or anger happen when we have so many feelings of discomfort that we use most of our energy to cover them up.

It's okay in some cases to suppress emotions. It's okay, for example, to ignore fear in the face of danger when fear might keep you from taking action to protect your family. Men and women process emotions differently, and this is okay. The important thing for men to remember is to show their emotions in healthy ways.

Children and adults receive messages all their lives that only certain feelings are good and that the majority of feelings are bad. The fact is that all feelings are okay. It's the way we show our feelings that can cause trouble. The same thing is true with the thoughts we have. All thoughts are okay. It's the way we act on our thoughts that counts.

The 3 Principles of Respect in Showing Emotions

1. **Respect yourself** - Don't hurt yourself.
2. **Respect others** - Don't hurt others.
3. **Respect the environment** - Don't disrespect your environment.

Session Log
Carrying Emotions

One new thing I learned today was_____
_____
_____
_____.

This information will help me become a better dad because_____
_____
_____
_____.

One way I will be a better dad is_____
_____
_____
_____.

Notes:
_____
_____
_____
_____
_____
_____

OPTIONAL Session 5.4

Recognizing Feelings of Grief and Loss

"Grief is itself a med'cine."
—William Cowper, (1731-1800)
Anti-Slavery Poet

"There are things we don't want to happen but have to accept, things we don't want to know but have to learn, and people we can't live without but have to let go."
—Author Unknown

Loss means to not have something any longer; to have something taken away by accident, carelessness, parting or death. Loss can refer to things you can touch, such as money, home, a person or a business, or to things you can't touch, such as love, health, status or a game.

Grief is the reaction people have to loss in their lives.

Grieving is the process of coming to terms with loss. Grieving also allows people to find new ways of coping with loss. Grieving can take years in some cases, like with the death of a child.

Men and women tend to grieve differently.

a. Men tend not to care for their emotions as well as women do.
b. Men tend to not want to be seen to care too much about their pain. Saying things like, 'It doesn't hurt that bad" or "I'm okay" are common.
c. Men tend to rely on women to help them deal with their emotions more than women rely on men for the same thing.

d. Men tend to need time away or want to be alone to think things through.
e. Men might show more anger.
f. Men might not show their grief in public.
g. Men grieve through ritual, such as doing or making something.

Grieving men can best help themselves by:

a. Showing courage by showing grief rather than covering it up.
b. Telling others about their need to be alone.
c. Not shutting others out.
d. Keeping communication open.
e. Tuning into their bodies and being aware of how their body reacts to grief.
f. Using rituals and actions to work through their grief.
g. Slowing down and thinking about what caused the grief.
h. Staying close to friends they can count on.
i. Making time to be outdoors.
j. Staying in good health and exercising.

Session Log
Recognizing Feelings of Grief and Loss

One new thing I learned today was_____

_____

_____

_____.

This information will help me become a better dad because_____

_____

_____

_____.

One way I will be a better dad is_____

_____

_____

_____.

Notes:

_____

_____

_____

_____

_____

_____

CORE Session 6.0
Love and Relationships

"The most important single ingredient in the formula of success is knowing how to get along with people."
—Theodore Roosevelt, the 26th President of the United States (1901-1909).

People have always looked for good relationships that have love and meaning. It is a basic human need to give and receive love from birth to death. But when it comes to love, it's knowing the who, what, where, when, why and how that's tough to figure out.

What are the main traits that go into making a long and healthy adult relationship?

_____

_____

_____.

For me, the two most important traits of a loving and good adult relationship are

_____ and _____

_____.

Exercise

What are or what would be the strengths of the relationship you currently have with your wife/partner (or would like to have with a future wife/partner)?

_____

_____

_____.

What areas might need to be worked on to improve your relationship (or that you need to work on for success in a future relationship)?

_____

_____

_____.

What is one thing you can do right away to improve your relationship (or prepare for a future relationship)?

_____

_____.

Session Log
Love and Relationships

One new thing I learned today was_____

_____

_____

_____.

This information will help me become a better dad because_____

_____

_____

_____.

One way I will be a better dad is_____

_____

_____

_____.

Notes:

_____

_____

_____

_____

_____

_____

OPTIONAL Session 6.1

The 7 Benefits of Marriage for Men

"The first bond of society is marriage."
—Marcus Tullius Cicero (106 B.C.– 43 B.C.),
Roman Politician and Philosopher

One benefit of marriage is _____

_____

_____

_____ because

_____

_____.

The 7 Benefits of Marriage for Men

1. Healthy Children
Children who grow up in a home with their two married parents are healthier, on average, than are children who grow up in a home in which their parents just live together. Children who grow up with their married parents are, for example, less likely to be abused and to misbehave in or drop out of school. These children are more likely to have good marriages of their own and to not wind up as a pregnant teen or to abuse alcohol or drugs. Marriage gives children the best chance at a healthy life!

2. Strong Relationships with Children
Marriage provides the best chance for fathers to create strong relationships with their children. Men who wait to have kids until they marry are three times more likely to be involved in their children's lives than are men who have kids outside of marriage. Dads who have good marriages are, on average, more involved in their children's lives than are never-married or divorced dads. That's because it's easier for married men to be with their children every day, and to nurture their kids at every stage of growth. Marriage can provide the joy of growing with your children every day!

3. Better Family Finances
Married couples have twice the money and assets that unmarried couples do. This can create a better financial future for couples and their children. And married men are more likely to save and invest, even when they have the same income as unmarried men. Marriage also comes with tax, inheritance and Social Security benefits. Marriage can help you make the most of your family's finances!

4. Fuller, Happier Lives
Married men are more likely to say they are happy than are unmarried men. After divorce, men are worse off overall than are women. The well-being of the family is the highest priority for most married men. When men focus on their wives and their children, not just on themselves, it helps them to lead full, happy lives. And married men are less likely to be depressed. Marriage gives men more family members they can turn to for social, emotional and financial support. Marriage can benefit you through a focus on the family!

5. A Long, Healthy Life
A full, happy life often leads to a long, healthy life. On average, married men live longer than do unmarried men. Married men are more likely to take care of themselves. They're more likely, for example, to stay in shape and to get medical help when they need it. And married

men are less likely to do things that can hurt them, such as smoking, drinking or using illegal drugs. Marriage can give you a great chance at a long, healthy life!

6. More, Better and Safer Sex

One sign of a full, happy life is an active, good and safe sex life. Married couples say they have sex more often than do unmarried people. And married men say they have better sex than do unmarried men. Married men work hard to build healthy relationships with their wives. They know that sex is best when they stay faithful to one woman. They also know that sex is best when they are emotionally close to their wives. And when a husband and a wife are faithful, sex is safer physically and emotionally. There is little chance that you will get a sexual disease if you and your wife are faithful. Marriage can give you the best chance for an active, great and safe sex life!

7. Increased Faithfulness

One reason that sex is better and safer in marriage is that married men and women are, on average, more faithful to each other than are men and women who simply live together or who date. You might be surprised to learn that most married men and women are faithful to each other. One study found that only 4 percent of wives are unfaithful compared to 20 percent of unmarried women who live with a man and 18 percent of women who date. Marriage can reduce the chance that the woman you love will cheat on you!

Adapted from The 7 Benefits of Marriage for Men Brochure published by National Fatherhood Initiative® © 2004.

Session Log
The 7 Benefits of Marriage for Men

One new thing I learned today was_____

_____

_____

_____.

This information will help me become a better dad because_____

_____

_____

_____.

One way I will be a better dad is_____

_____

_____

_____.

Notes:

_____

_____

_____

_____

_____

_____

OPTIONAL Session 6.2

Improving My Communication Skills

"There is nothing more admirable than two people who see eye-to-eye keeping house as man and wife, confounding their enemies, and delighting their friends."
—Homer, 9th century BC

My strength in communication is

_____

_____

_____.

My weakness in communication is

_____

_____

_____.

Problem Solving and Negotiation
Problem solving and negotiation are two vital skills in communication. Conversations often stall when parents and children have different ideas on what to do, what to wear, when to come home, etc.. When this happens, it can lead to fights. The goal is for parents and children to agree leaving both parties with power. Problem solving and negotiating can leave both parents and children feeling satisfied.

What is causing a problem between you and your child/children? (If you have never seen your children, imagine a problem that you might have with him or her.)

_____

_____

_____.

There is a difference between problem solving and decision-making.

Problem Solving
What you do when you have a problem, but don't know what the solution is.

Decision Making
What you do when you know what your options are.

Solving problems can be a "person process" (something a person does on his or her own) or a "family process" (where all family members help solve the problem). To take action in solving problems, you need to use the following steps.

Six Steps to Problem Solving
Step 1: Identify the problem.
Write the problem down for you or other family members to see. The first step is a vital one. Work on only one problem at a time. Have every family member agree on "the problem."

Step 2: Determine who owns the problem.
Is someone doing something you don't approve of, but who does not see the behavior as a problem? Is the problem yours or someone else's? Decide who owns the problem.

Step 3: Discuss what you have tried.
Talk with the person involved with the problem and review past efforts on solving the problem. Remember to use "I Statements" rather than blaming "You Statements."

An I Statement takes this form: "I feel _____ (say how you feel) when _____ (say what the person said or did) because_____ (say the reason for why you feel this way). What I need is _____ (say what you need for the person to do)." I Statements help you to own your feelings and keeps others from feeling they're to blame.

Step 4: Write down a goal statement.
What behavior do you want to see instead? This is the most crucial step and perhaps the hardest of them all. If it is a family member's problem, tell him or her the behavior you would like to see instead. Discuss the behavior you would like to see instead, and make sure the behavior is reasonable and can be done. Write down what you want to see, not what you don't want to see.

Step 5: Brainstorm ways to achieve what you would like to see instead.
Whether it is your problem or someone else's, brainstorm ways to get the desired behavior. This is an important step in solving problems.

Step 6: Make a decision.
Pick out your favorite three ways for solving the problem and use them to work on the desired behavior.

From the brainstormed ideas, the decision should be clear. If not, check the problem statement and the goal statement to make sure they reflect what you mean. If the problem still exists, begin the process with Step 1 again.

When this process does not resolve the issue, family members should use negotiation and compromise.

Session Log
Improving My Communication Skills

One new thing I learned today was_____

_____

_____

_____.

This information will help me become a better dad because_____

_____

_____

_____.

One way I will be a better dad is_____

_____

_____

_____.

Notes:

_____

_____

_____

_____

_____

_____

CORE Session 7.0
The Role of the Father

"My heroes are and were my parents. I can't see having anyone else as my heroes."
—Michael Jordan, NBA Legend

To me, **fathering** means_____

_____

_____.

To me, **mothering** means_____

_____

_____.

(Yesterday's Father) When I was growing up,

the role of the father in the family was_____

_____

_____

_____.

(Today's Father) I believe the role a father

should have in the family today is_____

_____

_____

_____.

Each of the following traits involves first looking at yourself and noticing whether there is a problem. The next step is deciding what to do to correct that problem. Putting these steps together creates a plan. We will discuss creating a plan in more detail later, but keep the following steps in mind as we go through the traits of the ideal father.

Plans Ahead
- Creates a plan for keeping in touch with his children.
- Sets achievable goals and follows through on them.
- Thinks about the long term while living in the present.
- Overcomes barriers to being a good father.

The InsideOut Dad™ program is based on five traits of the ideal father:

Self-Awareness
The InsideOut Dad…
- Is aware of the impact he has on his family.
- Is in touch with his moods, feelings and emotions.
- Knows his strengths and limits.
- Takes responsibility for his own behavior.
- Realizes that his personal growth is his responsibility.

The InsideOut Dad asks:
"How well am I doing in knowing myself?"

_____

_____.

Caring for Self

The InsideOut Dad…

- Is a man who takes care of himself.
- Lives a healthy lifestyle, including eating the right foods and getting exercise.
- Has a strong spiritual connection to his community.
- Chooses friends that support his healthy choices.
- Shows his children that he likes and respects himself by making good choices.

The InsideOut Dad asks:
"How well am I doing in taking care of myself?"

_____

_____ .

Fathering Skills

The InsideOut Dad…

- Is involved in the lives of his children.
- Is responsible for helping his children grow up to be good adults.
- Is committed to being a good dad to his children.
- Is very aware of the important role he plays in the lives of his children.
- Is a good role model.
- Supports his children's interests in sports, music and other activities.
- Knows the difference between "fathering" and "mothering" and why that difference is good for his children.

The InsideOut Dad asks:
"How well am I doing being a Father?"

_____

_____ .

Parenting Skills

The InsideOut Dad …

- Nurtures his children with love, affection and encouragement.
- Accepts how vital his parenting skills are to developing the physical, emotional, intellectual, social, spiritual and creative needs of his children.
- Creates a positive, trusting home where children grow with the support and love of a dad who cares for and nurtures them.
- Knows that discipline teaches and guides children, and is not used to physically and emotionally threaten or harm them.

The InsideOut Dad asks:
"How well am I doing being a parent?"

_____

_____ .

Relationship Skills

The InsideOut Dad…

- Builds and maintains healthy relationships with his children, wife/ mother of his children family and friends and community.
- Values the power of relationships to shape the characters of his children, and the quality of life he has with his wife/ mother of his children.
- Realizes that good, clear communication models appropriate behavior.
- Chooses healthy friends who all help shape the lives of his family members.

The InsideOut Dad asks:
"How well am I doing in my relationships?"

_____

_____ .

Session Log
The Role of the Father

One new thing I learned today was_____

_____

_____

_____.

This information will help me become a better dad because_____

_____

_____

_____.

One way I will be a better dad is_____

_____

_____

_____.

Notes:

_____

_____

_____

_____

_____

_____

_____

OPTIONAL Session 7.1
The Ideal Father

"When I was a boy of 14, my father was so ignorant I could hardly stand to have the old man around. But when I got to be 21, I was astonished at how much the old man had learned in seven years."
—Mark Twain

One memory I have of my father (or father figure) is_____

_____

_____.

What is unique about this memory is_____

_____

_____

_____.

Fathers have received bad press over the years for their "lack" of some traits. Terms like the "Absent Father," the "Abusive Father," and the "Deadbeat Dad" have all painted a bad portrait of dads. Can you think of other bad terms used to describe fathers?

_____

_____

_____.

The world clearly has its views of the way fathers "should be." In the following exercise, you will have the chance to create the "Ideal Father."

1. The **Qualities** of an ideal father. What does the ideal father provide to the family?
2. The **Traits** of an ideal father. What type of personality and traits does the ideal father have?
3. The **Responsibilities** of an ideal father. What responsibilities does the ideal father take on in his role?

"The Ideal Father"
1. **Qualities of the Ideal Father.** The ideal father provides the following to his family:

a. _____

b. _____

c. _____

d. _____

e. _____

f. _____

2. **Traits of the Ideal Father.** The ideal father has the following personality and traits:

a. _____

b. _____

c. _____

d. _____

e. _____

f. _____

3. Responsibilities of an Ideal Father. An ideal father takes on the following responsibilities:

a. _____

b. _____

c. _____

d. _____

e. _____

f. _____

How realistic are some of these qualities, traits and responsibilities?

_____

_____

_____.

Can any dad possess all these qualities, traits and responsibilities?

_____

_____

_____.

Which of these qualities, traits and responsibilities is it possible for the incarcerated father to have?

_____

_____

_____.

Thinking back when you were a little boy, which of these qualities, traits and responsibilities would you really have wanted your dad to have?

_____

_____

_____.

Which of these qualities, traits and responsibilities did your dad have?

_____

_____

_____.

Which of the qualities, traits and responsibilities would be good for dads not to have?

_____

_____

_____.

Session Log
The Ideal Father

One new thing I learned today was_____

_____

_____

_____.

This information will help me become a better dad because_____

_____

_____

_____.

One way I will be a better dad is_____

_____

_____

_____.

Notes:

_____

_____

_____

_____

_____

_____

OPTIONAL Session 7.2
Fathering and Culture

"The greatness of a nation and its moral progress can be judged by the way it treats its children."
—Author Unknown

Culture is a set of rules, beliefs, values and norms that guide a specific group of people at a specific point in time. Some examples of cultural groups are:

- Race (Black, White, Latino, Asian, etc.)
- Country of Origin (France, USA, Bolivia, etc.)
- Ethnicity (German, African, Chinese, etc.)
- Religion (Baptist, Catholic, Jewish, Islamic, etc.)
- Job and Careers (lawyer, carpenter, etc.)
- Gender (male or female)
- Age (youth, adolescent, adult, elder)
- Political (liberal, conservative, etc.)
- Income (rich, poor, etc.)
- Education (high school, college, etc.)
- Sports (golfers, swimmers, etc.)
- Music (rock, rap, etc)
- Art (film, media, etc.)

Some examples of "counter-cultures" would be:

_____.

Morals are the "rights and wrongs" of behaviors of an individual, family, culture or government. Morals are the "rights and wrongs" we learned as children.

One moral I learned in childhood that I still practice today is_____

_____

_____

_____, because _____

_____

_____.

One moral I learned in childhood that I don't practice today is _____

_____

_____, because _____

_____

_____.

One moral I teach my children that they practice is _____

_____

_____, because _____

_____

_____.

One moral I teach my children that they don't practice is _____

_____

_____

_____, because _____

_____

_____

_____ .

"Those who stand for nothing fall for anything."
—Alexander Hamilton, (1755-1804), one of the founding fathers and first Secretary of the U.S. Treasury

The "whys" to the morals that men and children practice or don't practice are directly tied to their values. (In other words, "why" you do something is tied to what is important to you.)

A **value** is something that has worth. Values as they relate to beliefs and behaviors are morals that have worth.

For morals and values to mean something, men must **model** morals and values, or "walk the talk." Modeling is a vital teacher of morals and values. Dads who say one thing but do another don't "walk the talk." Instead, they confuse children. The result is an example of a moral that has no positive value.

The model of not "walking the talk" or "do as I say and not as I do" does teach children a moral—a negative one.

When men don't do as they say, what are the children learning? _____

_____ .

What is the moral lesson the fathers are teaching? _____

_____ .

The bottom line is that children learn the "value" of not following through on commitments, on being disrespectful and being irresponsible.

Family Cultural Inventory

Complete the inventory by responding to each statement.

1. List three cultural values/traditions that you are passing on to your children. Describe what you do that models the value or tradition.

Cultural Value/Tradition: _____.

The way I model this value/tradition is: _____.

Cultural Value/Tradition: _____.

The way I model this value/tradition is: _____.

Cultural Value/Tradition: _____.

The way I model this value/tradition is: _____.

2. List three cultural practices/beliefs you would like to pass on to your children, but that you aren't doing a very good job with:

Cultural Practice/Belief:_____.

The actions I need to take to pass this practice/belief on are: _____

_____.

Cultural Practice/Belief:_____.

The actions I need to take to pass this practice/belief on are: _____

_____.

Cultural Practice/Belief:_____.

The actions I need to take to pass this practice/belief on are: _____

_____.

Session Log
Fathering and Culture

One new thing I learned today was_____

_____

_____

_____.

This information will help me become a better dad because_____

_____

_____

_____.

One way I will be a better dad is_____

_____

_____

_____.

Notes:

_____

_____

_____

_____

_____

_____

OPTIONAL Session 7.3
Competition & Fathering

"Fathers build the foundation of their children's successes." —Unknown

What **competition** means to me is _____

_____

_____

_____ .

What I like about competition is_____

_____ ,

because _____

_____ .

What I don't like about competition is _____

_____ ,

because _____

_____ .

Inventory on Competitive vs. Non-Competitive Fathering

Put a check mark by the trait that is "more like me" in each of the following categories. Answers with letter "a" suggest a competitive style. Answers with letter "b" suggest a less or non-competitive style.

1. Sports
___ a. Win at all costs
___ b. Have fun; improve skills

2. Grades
___ a. Insist on straight As
___ b. Study hard; do the best you can

3. Achievement
___ a. Never be satisfied
___ b. Take pride in accomplishments and pride yourself for your best efforts

4. Possessions
___ a. Bigger, better, faster, more expensive
___ b. Functional, useful, practical

5. Parenting
___ a. Always right; authoritative
___ b. Democratic

6. Relationships
___ a. Needs to be in control
___ b. Shares control

7. Efforts
___ a. Results matter more
___ b. It's not whether you win or lose but how you play the game

8. Career
___ a. Strives to move up at the expense of job satisfaction and family time
___ b. Advancement not as important as job satisfaction and time with family

Scoring the Competitive vs. Non-competitive Fathering Inventory

Add up the number of "a" answers. Then add up the number of "b" answers. Answers with the letter "a" suggest a competitive style of fathering. For example, if you answered "a" between:

5-8 suggests that you might have a very competitive fathering style.

3-4 suggests that you might have a slightly competitive fathering style.

1-2 suggests that you might not have a competitive fathering style.

Answers with the letter "b" suggest a noncompetitive style. In general, the more "b" answers you have the more balanced non-competitive style of fathering you have.

Session Log
Competition and Fathering

One new thing I learned today was_____

_____

_____

_____.

This information will help me become a better dad because_____

_____

_____

_____.

One way I will be a better dad is_____

_____

_____

_____.

Notes:

_____

_____

_____

_____

_____

_____

OPTIONAL Session 7.4
Fathering and Fun

"My father used to play with my brother and me in the yard. Mother would come out and say, 'You're tearing up the grass.' 'We're not raising grass,' Dad would reply. 'We're raising boys.'"
—Harmon Killebrew, Major League Baseball Hall of Famer

One memory I have of my Dad (or father figure) and I having fun is _____

_____

_____.

Ways my Dad (or father figure) and I would enjoy playing together were _____

_____

_____.

One way I would have liked to have had fun with my Dad (or father figure) was_____

_____

_____.

Many Dads find it hard to have fun with their children. Examples of things dads say are:
"You won't catch me acting like a kid."
"Having fun and acting like a kid is acting foolish."
"You won't catch me crawling around on the floor acting silly."

Why do some dads feel this way?

Negative Aspects of Humor, Laughter and Fun

Negative Humor
Humor that pokes fun at others; humor at the expense of others.

Negative Laughter
Laughter that pokes fun at others; laughing at the expense of others. (Example: Laughing when someone falls down.)

Negative Fun
Harmful actions or words aimed at physically or emotionally hurting others. (Examples: Tickling a child and not stopping at the child's request; pushing a child in the water.)

Positive Ways to have Fun with Children as a Part of Fathering

Reverse Psychology
In a happy and playful way, request the very behaviors you don't want. (Example: "Okay, I don't want to see anyone getting ready for bed. You have to sit there and not put your pj's on." Or, "I bet none of you guys can beat me up and stairs and get ready for bed!") Make it fun and watch the kids try to beat Dad up the stairs (the kids win).

Fooler Approach

This approach attempts to fool kids into learning the right behavior. (Example: "I bet I can fool you guys. I bet nobody here can brush their teeth all by themselves. No way – you guys can't do it!" Or, "I bet I can fool you guys. I bet nobody here knows our family rule about sharing things. I know it! Everybody is supposed to keep things and not share. Right?" Of course, the kids yell out, "No! Everyone is supposed to share things!" Dad then says, "Well, I sure couldn't fool you kids!") Kids love this game because they get to tell Dad he's wrong.

Talking Objects

Talking objects are a great way to get young kids to cooperate. (Example: Talking bathtub: "Oh Jessica, it's time to jump inside me and get nice and clean." Or, how about a piece of candy or a dessert that says, "No, no don't eat me now. Eat me after supper!")

Ways that I have increased my involvement in

my children's lives are _____

_____

_____.

The major benefit of this increased

involvement is _____

_____

_____.

Session Log
Fathering and Fun

One new thing I learned today was_____
_____
_____
_____.

This information will help me become a better dad because_____
_____
_____
_____.

One way I will be a better dad is_____
_____
_____
_____.

Notes:
_____
_____
_____
_____
_____

CORE Session 8.0
Building Self-Worth

"He who sets a very high value upon himself has the less need to be esteemed by others."
—Unknown

Self-concept
A man's **self-concept** is the thoughts he has about himself. A self-concept can be good or bad thoughts about parts of his life. A man might have a good self-concept of himself as a gardener, but a bad self-concept of himself as a cook. The self-concept varies with a man's roles. The man with an largely good self-concept thinks of himself in a positive way.

Self-esteem
A man's **self-esteem** is the feelings he has about himself. It means whether he holds himself in high esteem or low esteem. Messages we get from others affect our self-esteem.

Self-worth
A man's **self-worth** is the thoughts (self-concept) and feelings (self-esteem) that a man has about himself. The ways that a man can build his self-worth are like the ways that dads can help build self-worth in their children.

Mind Messages
Getting in touch with the good and bad messages that we send ourselves is a vital first step in building self-worth.

Examples:
  Bad: I'm not going to succeed.
  Good: I will succeed.

  Bad: She won't like me. I'm not good enough.
  Good: Even if she doesn't like me, I'm a good man and I value and like myself.

What is a bad message you send yourself?

_____

_____

_____.

The view we have of ourselves comes from our past, even as far back as childhood.

The mind forms habits in thinking. One way to break a "habit thought" is to think an opposite thought. Every time a bad message runs in your head, replace it with a good message.

Change your bad message into a good one and

write it here:_____

_____

_____.

Reminders

Using small notes, write words that reflect traits or behaviors you would like to develop. If you want to create respect between you and your wife or children, write the word "respect" on sticky notes and place them in areas in your daily life that you frequent. It's best if you work on one trait or behavior at a time.

When you practice or show your desired trait, make a mark or star on your note as a reward to yourself.

Do the same with behaviors or traits you want to encourage with other family members. Every time you see the trait or behavior, praise the person or the behavior, for example: "Thanks for cooperating" (Praise for Behavior) or "You really are a special person" (Praise for Being).

Make a mark or star on the note every time you see the desired trait or behavior. If you like, make a mark on another piece of paper of the times you saw an undesirable trait or behavior. Are you watching for these behaviors? Work to change your pattern.

Praise for Being

"I love you son. You are very special to me." Practice giving "Praise for Being" statements to all family members every day.

Praise for Behavior

"You did a great job cleaning your room!" Practice giving "Praise for Behavior" statements to all family members every day.

Self-Praise

Praise yourself for being and for doing every day.

Self-Praise for Being

"I'm a worthwhile person." "I'm a caring man."

Self-Praise for Behavior

"I'm doing a good job of listening to others." "I did a nice job cooking dinner."

And make it a habit to accept praise from others. A "thank you" is the polite way to receive and value a gift.

Experience Success

A good way to build self-worth as a man is to know what you are good at doing, and do more of it. You might not be aware of chances to succeed while incarcerated, but they do exist. You can, for example write to your children more often, get into a new class and study hard, write stories, draw pictures, read a book that you've always wanted to read. Success can be powerful even when the task is small. Success on small projects can give you the courage and experience to succeed at larger ones.

Be There for Others

A great way to build self-worth is to help others. Helping includes listening without interrupting, and valuing what another person has to say or believes, even if you don't agree with that person.

Which of the types of praise above do you

need to work on first?_____

_____.

Can you think of other ideas to help you build self-worth in yourself and your family?

_____

_____.

Session Log
Building Self-Worth

One new thing I learned today was_____

_____

_____

_____.

This information will help me become a better dad because_____

_____

_____

_____.

One way I will be a better dad is_____

_____

_____

_____.

Notes:

_____

_____

_____

_____

_____

_____

OPTIONAL Session 8.1
Career Expectations for My Children

"He who does not teach his son an occupation is as one who has taught his son to rob."
—Talmud (Rabbinical writings)

What does the word "career" mean to me?

_____

_____ .

What does the word "job" mean to me?

_____

_____ .

My last employment was a (job or career)

_____

_____

_____ .

Male vs. Female Work Roles
Please respond to this list by writing whether if you think the job or career is better suited for females (F), males (M) or both sexes (B).

___ Hairdresser
___ House Painter
___ Window Washer
___ Pro Basketball Player
___ Cab Driver
___ Teacher
___ Flight Attendant
___ Soldier
___ Maid
___ Referee
___ Bell Hop
___ Minister
___ Sales Clerk
___ Banker
___ CEO
___ Farmer
___ Pro Soccer Player
___ Airline Pilot
___ Singer
___ Parent
___ Musician
___ Construction Worker
___ Receptionist
___ Secretary
___ Nurse
___ Doctor
___ Dentist
___ Child Care Worker
___ Chef
___ Waiter
___ Sanitation Worker

Did you label some jobs only as male or

female?_____ .

Are some jobs and careers better suited for

one sex than the other? _____

_____.

The expectation I have for my son is that he
should have a (check one):
   ___ Career
   ___ Job

The career or job should be _____

_____

_____.

The expectation I have for my daughter is that
she should have a (check one)
   ___ Career
   ___ Job

The career or job should be _____

_____

_____.

Are the expectations you have for your sons
different than the expectations you have for
your daughters?

_____

_____

_____.

Are they different based only on your child's
sex?

_____

_____

_____.

Are the expectations you have of your children
related to things you haven't achieved in your
own life?

_____

_____

_____.

Session Log
Career Expectations for My Children

One new thing I learned today was_____

_____

_____

_____.

This information will help me become a better dad because_____

_____

_____

_____.

One way I will be a better dad is_____

_____

_____

_____.

Notes:

_____

_____

_____

_____

_____

CORE Session 9.0

Discipline and Styles of Discipline

"Disciplining children without first establishing a loving relationship leads to rebellion."
—Anonymous

One memory I have of being "disciplined" by my Dad (father figure or parents) is

_____

_____

_____.

What I learned from that experience was

_____

_____

_____.

Discipline

Discipline comes from a Latin word "discipulus" meaning "to teach or to guide." The follower of a teacher is called a "disciple." A disciple believes in the morals, values and behaviors of the teacher. A disciple practices what was taught by his or her teacher.

A father is a teacher—one who guides his children. Children are the disciples of their father. The father is a teacher of morals and values.

There are different types of teachers with different styles of teaching discipline. It is vital to remember that children learn in two ways:

1. From the time they spend with their teacher.
2. From watching their teacher's behavior.

Use the list below and pick out your style of discipline.
   a. Authoritarian
   b. Strict
   c. Dictator
   d. Permissive
   e. Wishy-washy
   f. Democratic
   g. King of the House
   h. Ruler
   i. Uninvolved
   j. Controlling
   k. Punitive
   l. Nurturing
   m. Easy
   n. Shaming
   o. Fair
   p. Other: _____

My style of teaching discipline to my children

would be called_____

_____.

My father's style of teaching discipline to me

was _____

_____.

My Discipline
(From My Children's Point of View)

In the box on below, take about 5-10 minutes to draw your style of discipline from your children's point of view. That is, how do you think your children see your style of discipline?

You can draw faces, designs, pictures, etc.

For discipline to be a good for you and your children, three factors are vital:

1. Bad styles that say your children are "no good" or "bad" are very harmful. When dads use shame, guilt, cruel words or blame, children don't learn that what they did is not okay, they learn that they are not okay.

2. Discipline must focus on the "action" not on the "actor." Any type of physical punishment says to children that they are a "bad person," and takes the focus away from the action.

3. After you have disciplined or punished your children, you must restore your relationship with them by saying that you still love them no matter what (you love them "unconditionally").

With my style of discipline, I want to make

sure my children learn _____

_____

_____.

What I'm afraid they might be learning is

_____

_____

_____.

Sometimes what we intend to teach is not always what children learn.

Session Log
Discipline and Styles of Discipline

One new thing I learned today was_____

_____

_____

_____.

This information will help me become a better dad because_____

_____

_____

_____.

One way I will be a better dad is_____

_____

_____

_____.

Notes:

_____

_____

_____

_____

_____

_____

OPTIONAL Session 9.1
Fathering, Power and Control

"He is most powerful who has control over himself."
—Seneca (5 B.C. – A.D. 65)

"With great power comes great responsibility."
—Unknown

To me, having control in my life means _____

_____

_____ .

One area I would like to have more control in

is _____ because _____

_____

_____ .

Power = strength, energy, authority
Power is the ability to exert strength or force on something or someone. Power has to do with a man's physical, mental and spiritual strength. Power can come with a man's position in life, such as with his job, and can be used in good and bad ways.

Control = regulate or restrain
Control is the ability to direct, restrain or influence your own and others' feelings, emotions and life. Men sometimes use their power to control others, which includes using their position in life to control others.

Power and Control Inventory
1. As a man, the ways I use my power in good

ways are_____

_____ ,

and the ways I use my power in bad ways are

_____

_____ .

2. As a dad, the good ways I control my

children are_____

_____ ,

and the bad ways I control my children are

_____

_____ .

3. As a husband/partner, the ways I use my

power in good ways are_____

_____ ,

and the ways I use my power in bad ways are

_____

_____ .

Session Log
Fathering, Power and Control

One new thing I learned today was_____

_____

_____

_____.

This information will help me become a better dad because_____

_____

_____

_____.

One way I will be a better dad is_____

_____

_____

_____.

Notes:

_____

_____

_____

_____

_____

_____

OPTIONAL Session 9.2
Culture, Morals and Discipline

"One generation plants the trees; another gets the shade."
—Chinese Proverb

One tradition my Dad (parents) passed on to me that I would like to pass on to my children is _____

_____

_____.

The reason I would like to pass this tradition on is _____

_____

_____.

Culture is a set of rules, beliefs, values and norms that guide a specific group of people at a specific point in time. Some examples of cultural groups are:

   a. Race (Black, White, Latino, Asian, etc.)
   b. Country of Origin (France, USA, Bolivia, etc.)
   c. Ethnicity (German, Nigerian, Chinese, etc.)
   d. Religion (Baptist, Catholic, Methodist, Muslim, etc.)
   e. Job and Careers (lawyer, carpenter, etc.)
   f. Gender (male or female)
   g. Age (youth, adolescent, adult, elder)
   h. Political (liberal, conservative, etc.)
   i. Income (rich, poor, welfare, etc.)
   j. Education (high school, college, etc.)
   k. Sports (golfers, swimmers, etc.)
   l. Music (rock, rap, etc.)
   m. Art (film, media, etc.)

Some examples of "counter-cultures" would be:

   a. Drug users
   b. Tax evaders
   c. Terrorists
   d. Gangs

Why do people choose to be "counter culture?"

Morals are the "rights and wrongs" we learned as children. These morals are a part of our culture and are passed down through our families and other important people in our lives. As a result, culture drives the morals we learned as children.

One moral I learned in childhood that I still practice today is _____

_____

because_____

_____.

One moral I learned in childhood that I don't practice today is _____

_____

because_____

_____.

One moral I teach my children that they

practice is _____

_____

because_____

_____.

One moral I teach my children that they don't
practice is _____

_____

because_____

_____.

The "whys" to the morals that dads and
children practice or don't practice are affected
by values. (In other words, "why" you do
something is related to what is important to
you.)

Session Log
Culture, Morals and Discipline

One new thing I learned today was_____

_____

_____

_____.

This information will help me become a better dad because_____

_____

_____

_____.

One way I will be a better dad is_____

_____

_____

_____.

Notes:

_____

_____

_____

_____

_____

_____

OPTIONAL Session 9.3
Being a Fair and Loving Father

"Live so that when your children think of fairness and integrity, they think of you."
—H. Jackson Brown, Jr., Author of "A Father's Book of Wisdom"

The way I was disciplined growing up was

_____

_____

_____.

What I liked about it was _____

_____

_____.

What I didn't like about it was _____

_____

_____.

To me, discipline should _____

_____

_____.

Many men feel that discipline means "to control" rather than "to teach or to guide." As a result, some dads use fear to punish their children. Examples include: threats of the loss of love, safety, belonging, privileges, etc.

Discipline needs to be clear, consistent and doable. To achieve this goal, you must establish Family Rules. The purpose of Family Rules is to ensure that children succeed in discipline.

Steps in Establishing Family Rules

Step 1: Call a family meeting.

Step 2: Explain that all family members are going to help establish the Family Rules.

Step 3: Divide a large sheet of paper (poster board) into halves by drawing a line down the middle.

Step 4: Label one side DOs and the other side DON'Ts . For every DON'T, there needs to be a DO, otherwise children are learning only DONTs.

Step 5: Get the rules from the children. Ask, "What kind of rule should we have about ____?" Issues might be homework, hanging up clothes, calling home when you're going to be late, etc.

Step 6: Come up with a DO (such as, Do homework before dinner.) and a DONT (such as, Don't wait until after supper to do your homework.).

Step 7: Keep the list to around 5 to 7 rules. Too many rules can be confusing to children.

Every rule needs a consequence so that children learn the basic idea of discipline. A

simple formula is "If-Then" as in, "If you do _____, then _____ will happen." The If-Then formula helps children learn to make good choices.

The reason to punish is to provide a bad consequence to an bad behavior so that children will learn to replace that behavior with an good one.

Rewards and Punishments

For your children to learn good behaviors, you need to reward them. Rewards create the value in your children to behave in the right way.

There are five types of Rewards and Punishments that help children learn right from wrong (morals). These are not punishments like slapping, yelling or bribing children that teach children that they—not their behavior—are bad. These five good consequences (Rewards) and bad consequences (Punishments) also help you teach your children the value of treating others with respect.

Rewards
Praise
Praise your children for behaving in the right way (what they do) and praise them with love (who they are).

Gentle Touch
Give your children hugs, massages, pats, high fives, etc.

Privileges
Allow your children to stay up later, have extra story time, etc.

Objects
Give your children toys, stickers, etc.

Allowance
To help children ten years and older manage their money. Give an allowance for chores done.

Punishments
Being Grounded
Children can't leave the house, for example, because they left the house without asking or they broke curfew.

Time-Out
Children are placed in a chair away from others for a brief period of inactivity when they violate the Family Rules, morals or values.

Loss of Privilege
Children lose a privilege when they misuse an object or privilege on purpose.

Restitution ("Paying Back")
Children must clean up a mess, replace an object broken on purpose, perform in-home community service (such as cleaning a fish tank, raking leaves or vacuuming), etc.

Parental Disappointment
You tell your children how disappointed you are for a bad decision or action done and that they meant to do.

Session Log
Being a Fair and Loving Father

One new thing I learned today was_____

_____

_____

_____.

This information will help me become a better dad because_____

_____

_____

_____.

One way I will be a better dad is_____

_____

_____

_____.

Notes:

_____

_____

_____

_____

_____

_____

CORE Session 10.0

Developmental Stages of Childhood

"There is a greater difference from the infant to the speaking child than there is from the schoolboy to an Einstein."
—Anonymous

Nature:
The traits a person is born with (height, race, color of hair, learning abilities, special learning needs, gender, DNA, etc.)

Nurture:
The way a child is treated during childhood that strongly influences the development of his or her personality.

Nature vs. Nurture

Do people turn out to be the way they are because of nature or because of nurture?

People have asked the nature versus nurture question for hundreds of years. Today, it's known that people are the way they are because nature and nurture act as one. The way parents and culture raise children can strengthen a natural trait or weaken it. Parents and culture can support or hold back children's talents. Talents "shine" when they are nurtured and weaken when they are neglected or punished.

Much the same holds true with children's abilities at each stage of growth. Like any building, the foundation of a child's growth is vital. When children get off to a good start, it raises the chance they will grow in healthy ways.

Ages and Stages

(See the Appendix for the milestones for your children's ages.)

There are two key points to know about the "Ages and Stages" information listed in the Appendix:

1. **These charts can scare some parents.** Don't let the charts scare you. They can be helpful. The fact is that there is too much information on child growth to know it all without looking to the charts for help. Even pediatricians (doctors for children) keep these kinds of charts to refer to in their work!

2. **Don't use these charts like report cards.** Don't use them to compare your children to other children or to each other. They are only road maps to guide you about the things children should be able to do at a certain age. All children grow differently. The most vital thing is that your children do these things sooner or later. If you are ever worried about how your child is growing, talk with your child's doctor.

Session Log
Developmental Stages of Childhood

One new thing I learned today was_____

_____

_____

_____.

This information will help me become a better dad because_____

_____

_____

_____.

One way I will be a better dad is_____

_____

_____

_____.

Notes:

_____

_____

_____

_____

_____

_____

OPTIONAL Session 10.1
Expectations and Self-Worth

"A master can tell you what he expects of you. A teacher awakens your own expectations."
—Unknown

One childhood expectation my parents had for

me that I was able to achieve was _____

_____, and in meeting

this expectation I felt _____

_____.

One childhood expectation my parents had

for me that I was unable to achieve was _____

_____, and in not

meeting this expectation I felt _____

_____.

Self-worth is the value a person has for himself. Self-worth is a person's **self-concept** (thoughts about himself) and **self-esteem** (feelings about himself) combined.

An overall self-worth is pretty solid over time. Still, a self-concept or self-esteem can move between good or bad (or high or low) based on events in a person's life.

Parental expectations are the behavior and abilities that parents expect from their children.

When expectations can't be met, what is likely to happen to the child's self-worth?

_____

_____.

When expectations are met, what is likely to happen to a child's self-worth?

_____

_____.

Session Log
Expectations and Self-Worth

One new thing I learned today was_____

_____

_____

_____.

This information will help me become a better dad because_____

_____

_____

_____.

One way I will be a better dad is_____

_____

_____

_____.

Notes:

_____

_____

_____

_____

_____

_____

OPTIONAL Session 10.2

Differences Between the Male and Female Brain

"Vive la difference!"
—French Saying

How would you answer the following statements?

a. The brains of males are different from the brains of females. True or False?

b. The male brain tends to be geared for talking rather than for doing. True or False?

c. The brain secretes serotonin, which is a chemical that calms us down. Men have less serotonin than women. True or False?

d. Girls would rather play with dolls while boys would rather throw a ball around. This is learned behavior. True or False?

e. Testosterone is the hormone related to higher levels of sexual energy and aggression in males. True or False?

f. Try as you might, females remember more than males. True or False?

g. Men's brains take different mental "naps" than women's brains. True or False?

h. Some violence is intentional. True or False?

i. No matter what you do, males will be more violent that females. True or False?

Answers:

a. **True.** While male and female brains are set up with the same three parts (brainstem, limbic system and neocortex), there is a difference in the size and function of male and female brains.

b. **False.** Male brains tend toward development of complex spatial skills, such as mechanical design, direction, measurement and manipulation of physical objects. Surges of testosterone in the womb and at puberty are largely responsible for this tendency.

c. **True.** As a result, men tend to act more impulsively than women. While women

produce more serotonin than men, they use up their store of it more quickly and replace it less quickly than do men.

d. **True and False.** The brains of girls generally secrete a higher level of oxytocin, a brain chemical that causes us to bond and feel empathic. Based on higher levels of serotonin (calming) and oxytocin (bonding), girls generally spend more time relating to others in a more calm way than do boys. Boys tend to be more active and less verbal than are girls. Social factors also play a role. We expect girls and boys to have different interests.

e. **True.** Men have up to 20 times more testosterone than women.

f. **True.** The memory center in women is larger than in men.

g. **True.** Women's brains are constantly working. Men's brains "zone out" and take more mental naps (for example, zoned out in front of the TV).

h. **True.** Brain chemicals responsible for preparing the body for "fight or flight" play a major role in aggression and violence.

i. **False.** Social conditioning can help boys increase their ability to bond and decrease their abilities toward violence.

Session Log
Differences Between the Male and Female Brain

One new thing I learned today was_____

_____

_____

_____.

This information will help me become a better dad because_____

_____

_____

_____.

One way I will be a better dad is_____

_____

_____

_____.

Notes:

_____

_____

_____

_____

_____

CORE Session 11.0

Creating a Fathering Plan

"There is no secret to success. It is the result of preparation, hard work, and learning from failure."
—Colin Powell, Former Chairman of the U.S. Joint Chiefs of Staff (1989-93) and U.S. Secretary of State (2001-2004)

You are nearing the end of the InsideOut Dad™ program. It's time to show your child what you've learned and put it into action. Every piece of your plan begins with a "what," as in what you plan to do, followed by a "how," as in how you plan to do it. Below are some basic tips to help you start your plan. Feel free to come up with your own ideas on how to be a father on the inside.

Become an Expert on Your Children
"It is a wise father who knows his own child."
—Shakespeare

Well, your children are growing up fast. Before you know it, they will be all grown up with kids of their own. Take this time on the inside to learn as much as you can about your kids. Use the Appendix in this handbook to learn about your children's stage of growth. Your prison library should have books, videos or other items that can help you learn about what your children should be doing at their ages. Discuss what you learn the next time you write or talk on the phone to your children. The more you know about what is happening in your children's lives, the more they will open up to you. If there is anything about your children that you don't know, take time to find out!

Here are some sample questions about your children. Try to answer them. (If you have more than one child, answer each question for each child.)

When is your child's birthday?

_____.

What is your child learning in school this semester?

_____.

What is your child's favorite school subject?

_____.

Does your child like to play sports? If yes, which ones?

_____.

What is your child's favorite cartoon character?

_____.

Who is your child's best friend?

_____.

What grade is your child in and what is the name of your child's teacher?

_____.

What is your child's favorite book?

_____.

QUESTION!
What are some other things you think a good dad should know about his children?

_____

_____

_____.

PLAN!
What will you do to become a better expert on your children?

_____

_____

_____.

How will you do become an expert?

_____

_____

_____.

Become a "Long Distance" Coach
If your children like basketball or some other sport or activity, learn all you can about it. What are the skills that someone needs to play it, and what are the rules? Which athletes do your children look up to? When you stay

on top of what is going on in your children's favorite activities, you can share more in letters, phone calls and during visits. It's a great way to be a part of your child's growth, even though you can't be with them.

If you want to move beyond just being a coach, there are some great games you can play with your children through the mail. Chess, for example, is a fun and easy game for kids to learn and play by mail. If you wanted to do something a little more active, you could set up a contest between you and your children where you try to pick the winners from each week's football game schedule. Be as creative as you can and remember that having fun with your children is what it's all about!

QUESTION!
Can you think of any other types of long distance activities you could do with your children?

_____

_____

_____.

PLAN!
What will you do to become a long distance coach for your children?

_____

_____

_____.

How will you become a coach?

_____

_____

_____ .

Help Your Children Take Care of Their Physical Health

"He who has health, has hope; and he who has hope, has everything."
—Arabian Proverb

Do you want your children to feel good about themselves and live healthy lives? Of course you do.
Here are some simple ways you can encourage your children to maintain a healthy lifestyle:

- Encourage your children to exercise as much as possible. Maybe they can even join a team or play an individual sport.
- Promote the benefits of eating healthy foods.

- Talk to your children about the dangers of smoking, drugs and alcohol.
- Let them know how you are taking care of yourself.

QUESTION!
What are some things you could do to improve your physical health?

_____

_____

_____ .

PLAN!
What will you do to take better care of your physical health?

_____

_____

_____ .

How will you encourage your children to take better care of their physical health?

_____

_____

_____ .

Promote Emotional Growth
Helping your children grow emotionally might be the hardest job you face while you're on the inside. It's hard because it means showing emotions that might lead others to think you're weak. It's also hard because to care for your child's emotional growth, you have to grow emotionally, too. But don't worry…you can do it! Be open to talking about your hopes and dreams for yourself and your children.

Tell your children that you love and accept them no matter what. Your children will feel wanted, accepted and loved when you show your love.

Don't mess around with you children's emotions. Using emotions like guilt, shame and pity to get attention from your children is not healthy. Children learn how to treat others by the way they are treated. Choose your words and actions carefully. They will have a lasting impact on your children's lives.

Learn to show your emotions without expecting something in return. Being a father means sacrifice and putting the well-being of your children above your own. True love will draw your children to you. Be open and let your children know how you truly feel.

QUESTION!
What are some things you could do to get closer to your children?

_____

_____

_____.

PLAN!
What will you do to help your children with his their emotional growth?

_____

_____

_____.

How will you help your children in this area?

_____

_____

_____.

Promote Spiritual Growth
Talk to your children about what it takes to make a spiritual family. Remember, a "spiritual family" is one that feels membership for all of its members and where members feel that they belong. When "family spirituality" is present, members cooperate, love and respect each other.

Tell your children about your spiritual beliefs. Learn more about your own spiritual beliefs and share what you've learned with your children. Tell your children how your faith teaches you not only what is right and wrong, but why something is right or wrong.

QUESTION!
Count your blessings! Can you name some things that you are thankful for?

_____

_____

_____.

PLAN!
What will you do to promote your children spiritual growth?

_____

_____

_____.

How will you help your children in this area?

_____

_____

_____.

Commit to Improving Yourself

Be a role model. Fathers are role models to their children, whether they realize it or not. Despite being on the inside, there are still many things you can teach your children about what is important in life. When you model honesty, humility, responsibility and commitment, you teach your children that even in hard times, it is vital to have strong moral values.

Take a class or join a study group and learn something new. Most places offer inmates classes or other ways to study a subject. Show your chidlren that you can make the best out of hard times and learn something new in the process.

Take responsibility for your words and actions. Sometimes, the children of dads in prison think that they somehow play a role in the reasons why their dad is on the inside. It's important that you let your children know that you are responsible for your own actions and that your children have nothing to do with where you are now. Showing your children that you can be responsible for your words and actions teaches them that honesty, self control, discipline and respect are keys to success in life.

Learn from the past. The adults in your past might not have been very responsible. The way they treated you as a child helped to shape the kind of person you are today. Take some time to think back to when you were a child. Do you remember how things affected you? Remember, learn and grow. Even though you have made some mistakes, you have a great chance to be the kind of dad you always wanted as a child. Good luck!

PLAN!
What will you do to improve yourself?

_____

_____

_____.

How will you improve yourself?

_____

_____

_____.

Adapted from *Staying Involved with Your Children While Incarcerated,* a brochure published by the National Fatherhood Initiative[SM] © 2004

Session Log
Creating a Fathering Plan

One new thing I learned today was_____

_____

_____

_____.

This information will help me become a better dad because_____

_____

_____

_____.

One way I will be a better dad is_____

_____

_____

_____.

Notes:

_____

_____

_____

_____

_____

OPTIONAL Session 11.1
Understanding Mentoring Programs

"We must break the cycle of incarceration so that it does not continue from one generation to the next."
—Jim Doyle, the 44th Governor of Wisconsin

What happens to a child when his or her dad goes to prison?

a. **The Dad and Child Live Apart**: The child is cut off from the dad. The child must live with the other parent, grandparents or even in foster homes.

b. **The Child Feels Badly**: The child can feel many emotions from sadness to shame and anger. Often, the child feels badly about him or herself, gets depressed, withdraws, acts out and starts to abuse alcohol and drugs.

c. **The Dad and Child Lose Touch Over Time**: After they go to prison, dads rarely see their children. They might talk with their children with phone calls, write letters or have personal visits. But the longer the dad's sentence, the less often he has contact with the child over time.

d. **The Child Winds Up in Prison**: A child of a dad in prison is at high risk for repeating criminal behavior. It's sad, but many children of dads in prison go to prison, just like their dads.

e. **The Single Parent Looks for Options**: Many families across our country are turning to mentoring programs to help them meet the demands of raising a child with one parent in prison.

What is "mentoring?"
Mentoring is matching a child of incarcerated parents with a caring adult who personally spends one-on-one time with the child. Adult mentors can help a young person in many ways. By spending time together, the child and adult mentor can talk about how making good choices everyday can lead to a bright future.

QUESTION!
Were there any adults, other than your parents, who spent quality time with you as a child? If yes, who were they?

_____

_____.

Where do they find the adults that will be mentoring your child?
Signing up and training mentors is taken very seriously.

- Churches and volunteer organizations carefully find qualified adults who want to mentor young people.
- Experience counts – Each adult's personal background is carefully examined.
- Each volunteer must complete a criminal background check.
- Community organizations like Big Brothers, Big Sisters help by selecting, training and supervising mentors.

Remember that the mentors need the support of both parents if they are to succeed in building a good relationship with the child.

How are children spending time with their mentors?

- Mentors often take the children to movies, cultural events, ball games, restaurants, youth activities, church, family activities, fun stuff at the park.
- Mentors and children meet 2-4 times per month for an average of 7-8 hours per month.
- Most relationships continue for at least one year.

QUESTION!

What are some fun things that you wanted to do as a child but never did?

_____

_____.

Why did you never get the chance?

_____

_____.

How do children benefit from mentoring?

Mentoring programs for children of incarcerated parents have shown good results.

When the mentor-youth relationship lasts at least 12 months:
- Young children get to go to new places and try new things.
- As their experiences grow, the children gain a greater sense of what is possible in the world.
- Children will be more self-confident about their school work, which leads to better grades.
- Young children are less likely to start using drugs or alcohol.
- Children are less likely to go to jail.

The bottom line is that children who stay in mentoring programs increase their chances of success.

Session Log
Understanding Mentoring Programs

One new thing I learned today was_____

_____

_____

_____.

This information will help me become a better dad because_____

_____

_____

_____.

One way I will be a better dad is_____

_____

_____

_____.

Notes:

_____

_____

_____

_____

_____

_____

OPTIONAL Session 11.2
Paper Hugs from Daddy

"You can't give a hug without getting a hug."
—Unknown

"Hugging has no unpleasant side effects and is all natural. There are no batteries to replace and no monthly payments. It's non-taxable, non-polluting, and is, of course, fully refundable."
—Unknown

When was the last time you gave someone a hug?

_____

_____.

Every child loves a good hug. Can you explain why?

_____

_____.

How do hugs make children feel inside?

_____

_____.

Did you remember getting many hugs as a child?

_____

_____.

How did they make you feel?

_____

_____.

Everyone loves a good hug from time to time. To children, a hug from dad, means "somebody in the world loves me." It has been said that when a parent hugs their child, for that split second everything in the world is okay. In this session, you will learn how to create a paper "hug" to send to your children.

"A hug is a great gift - one size fits all, and it's easy to exchange."
—Unknown

Just imagine how much your child will enjoy getting this unique gift that only you could give. You don't have to be an artist. Use lots of colors and decorate it anyway you like. Just be sure to decorate it with lots of love. Remember that no matter how you hug looks, your children will get the message that you love them very much.

Session Log
Paper Hugs from Daddy

One new thing I learned today was_____

_____

_____

_____.

This information will help me become a better dad because_____

_____

_____

_____.

One way I will be a better dad is_____

_____

_____

_____.

Notes:

_____

_____

_____

_____

_____

_____

OPTIONAL Session 11.3
Reading to Your Kids on Tape, Video or CD

"The more that you read, the more things you will know. The more that you learn, the more places you'll go."
—Dr. Seuss (1904-1991)

"Reading is to the mind what exercise is to the body."
—August Hare, English Clergyman (1792-1834)

What was your favorite children's book when you were a kid?

_____.

Why? What did you like about it?

_____

_____

_____.

The Benefits of Reading Books to Your Children on Tape, Video or CD:
Reading books on audio tape is a great way for a dad to reconnect or to start a relationship with his children.

If you had a relationship with your children before you went to prison, this activity provides a great opportunity for you a chance to re-connect with your children.

If you have young children (under the age of 4 or so), this activity will help your children read from an early age and help them get ready for school.

Your children will get used to your voice, which will help you re-enter their lives more easily when you're on the outside

"Today a reader, tomorrow a leader"
—Margaret Fuller (1810-1850)

How to Get Started Recording Your Book
1. Before you begin, you must first write a letter to your child's care giver (such as, mother, grandmother, grandfather) seeking his or her cooperation.

2. After your child's care giver has agreed to cooperate, you should check with corrections staff to gain access to a:
   1) tape recorder and audio cassettes,
   2) video recorder and video cassettes, or
   3) CDs and a computer with microphone and recordable CD drive.

3. After you have the right equipment, then you can select a children's book to read on tape. You should choose a book that is suitable for your child's age and one that your child would enjoy reading.

4. Before recording yourself reading the book, you might want to practice reading the book a few times.

5. Be sure to say hello to your child on the tape before reading the story, and tell your child goodbye when you finish reading it.

6. After you record the book, you should put the cassette/video cassette/CD and children's book into an addressed, stamped, unsealed padded envelope or mail bag, and then give the package to corrections staff for security clearance. After it has been cleared, corrections staff will place the package in the mail for pick up and delivery.

7. When your child receives the recording and the book in the mail, he or she will be able to listen to the story and follow along in the book. Because your child owns the recording, he or she will be able to listen to the tape over and over again, and in the process, get used to hearing your voice.

Session Log
Reading to Your Kids on Tape, Video or CD

One new thing I learned today was_____

_____

_____

_____.

This information will help me become a better dad because_____

_____

_____

_____.

One way I will be a better dad is_____

_____

_____

_____.

Notes:

_____

_____

_____

_____

_____

_____

                                          www.fatherhood.org

OPTIONAL Session 11.4
Chess By Mail

"Every chess master was once a beginner."
—Irving Chernev, Great Chess Author

"Just as every pawn is a potential Queen, every child is a potential King."
—C. L. Barbe

10 Reasons Why You Should Play Chess with Your Children
Share these life lessons with your children as you play chess together.

1. **Children like chess and it makes them smarter!** Legend has it that chess was invented to train the royal children of an Indian king on the tactics of military strategy. Nearly 2000 years later, children are still playing chess and learning in the process. Many studies have proven that children who play chess do better at math and reading and do better in school than children who don't play the game. It's simple; children who play chess do better in school and have a better chance to succeed in life. Besides all that, beating your dad at chess is just plain fun!

2. **Chess teaches you to learn from your mistakes.** Former World Champion, Jose Raul Capablanca once said, "You may learn much more from a game you lose than from a game you win. You will have to lose hundreds of games before becoming a good player."

3. **Chess teaches you the consequences of actions.** In chess, as in life, you can't take back your moves after you make them. Weighing the strengths and weaknesses of your position, and thinking before you move, is the key to success in life and the game. In chess, you control your own fate.

4. **Chess promotes thinking for yourself.** Players are forced to trust their own judgment and to think for themselves. Like life, the more players know about the rules of the game, the better decisions they are going to make.

5. **Chess is good for your mental health.** People who play games like chess on a regular basis are 2.5 times less likely to get Alzheimer's disease.

6. **Chess can be played over long distances.** Dads and children can play chess by mail (called "correspondence chess"). Simply take turns, mailing moves to each other, one move per letter. It takes some time to complete a game, but it is a great way for dads and their children to stay connected and have fun at the same time.

7. **Chess teaches you how to think strategically.** The game involves seeing problems and finding the answers. Being able to think strategically is a great tool for anyone who wants to move from where they are to where they want to be.

8. **Chess teaches you to move beyond the surface and dig deep to find the buried treasure.** Good chess players search for the best move at all times. Sometimes this means putting in a little more thought and effort. But the rewards are often greater when you

take the time to find the right move in chess and in life.

9. **Chess teaches you patience.** Chess is game where the rules of the game can be learned in minutes, but it can't be mastered in a life time. Chess is a game you can actually play for the rest of your life.

10. **Chess is an international game.** Chess is a language spoken in every part of the globe. Chess doesn't care who you are or where you came from. From the penthouse suites to the streets, chess knows no limits. All you need is a board, some chess pieces, a sharp mind and someone to play against.

Session Log
Chess By Mail

One new thing I learned today was_____

_____

_____

_____.

This information will help me become a better dad because_____

_____

_____

_____.

One way I will be a better dad is_____

_____

_____

_____.

Notes:

_____

_____

_____

_____

_____

_____

CORE Session 12
Ending the Program

"To map out a course of action and follow it to an end requires courage."
—Ralph Waldo Emerson, American Poet, Lecturer and Essayist (1803-1882)

When I recall my childhood, one way my Dad (caregiver) was involved in my life was

_____

_____

_____

_____.

One way I wish my Dad (caregiver) had been more involved was

_____

_____

_____

_____.

One way that I am involved in my children's lives is

_____

_____

_____

_____.

What this involvement means to me is _____

_____

_____ and what it means to

my children is _____

_____

_____

_____

_____.

"Other things may change us, but we start and end with family."
—Anthony Brandt

Ways Dads Can Be Involved Checklist
Please circle the word that best describes your involvement with your children.

1. Writing letters to your kids.

    None   Little   Often   A Lot

2. Calling your kids.

    None   Little   Often   A Lot

3. Visits with your kids.

    None   Little   Often   A Lot

4. Reading stories to your children on audio, video or CD.

    None   Little   Often   A Lot

5. Learning about how your children do in school.

    None   Little   Often   A Lot

6. Learning your children's likes and dislikes

    None   Little   Often   A Lot

7. Telling your children you love them

    None   Little   Often   A Lot

8. Teaching your children about your beliefs.

    None   Little   Often   A Lot

9. Learning about your child's interests.

    None   Little   Often   A Lot

10. Being a long distance coach.

    None   Little   Often   A Lot

One thing I'm going to miss about this group is

_____

_____

_____

_____.

When I think about all the sessions in the program, the most important thing I learned that will help me become a better dad is

_____

_____

_____

_____.

Session Log
Ending the Program

One new thing I learned today was_____

_____

_____

_____.

This information will help me become a better dad because_____

_____

_____

_____.

One way I will be a better dad is_____

_____

_____

_____.

Notes:

_____

_____

_____

_____

_____

_____

Reentry
Creating Your Reentry Plan

"Plans must be simple and flexible... They should be made by the people who are going to execute them."
—George S. Patton, Jr., World War II General

As you write action steps to achieve each item below, assign dates to each step and check them off as you complete them. Feel free to use extra paper to write other steps to take. You can change and add to this plan as much and as often as you like.

1. Believe You Can Succeed
"The dictionary is the only place where success comes before work."
—Anonymous

It's easy to get down because there are things you can't control while you're on the inside and when you first get home. But don't lose hope. Keep looking for answers to your challenges. The more time you spend thinking about what you have and can do, the easier it will be to succeed on the outside.

Write down what inspires you to succeed:

_____

_____

Write down what you will do to succeed:

_____

_____

2. Know Where You are Going to Live
This is easier said than done. The best-laid plans for housing sometimes fall apart at the last moment and can threaten your success. Know what your housing options are. Family members are often the best option, but you need to tell them about your plans now and not wait to the last minute to ask for a place to stay. Plans to stay away from the people, places or things that remind you of your troubled past often don't work. You might be drawn back to what and who you know, so it's better to surround yourself with good people from your past who will support you than to avoid your past entirely.

Write down where you plan to live after release or what you will do to find a place to live:

_____

_____

_____

3. Tell Your Family about Your Release Date and Plans
Your reentry will be much easier if you have the support of your family. Telling them when you will be released and how you plan to get your life in order will help them to help you. Send your reentry plan to them. Prepare to change and add to your reentry plan as you move closer to release.

Write down who you will contact and when. After you complete these contacts, check them off:

_____

_____

_____

4. Respect Your Children's Mother

Whether you are married to the mother of your children or not, it's vital that you keep a good relationship with her. Even if you don't always get along with her, show her respect because that's good for your children. Set aside your problems with her for the good of your children. If you are married to her, love her with all your heart. One of the best things a dad can do for his children is to love their mom.

Write down ways you can show your respect for your children's mother:

_____

_____

_____

5. Contact Your Children

Contact your children as soon as you can and as often as possible. Your children need you to be their dad, even if you don't live with them. If you're on the inside, be sure to write, call or to have them in for visits as often as you can.

Write down ways you plan to contact your children:

_____

_____

_____

6. Be a Role Model

You might have made some bad choices in life and paid for them. Now is your chance to create a new life—a life that is a model for your children to help them not make the same mistakes. Show your kids that you can change your life. It will be one of the best lessons you'll ever teach them. Also show them that you can take responsibility for your actions. Follow the rules and be responsible while on the inside and after your release. Your children will learn that even when you make mistakes, you can learn from them.

Write down ways that you can be a role model:

_____

_____

_____

7. Get an ID

If you or a family member doesn't have your driver's license, state photo ID, passport or birth certificate, ask your counselor or another staff member about what you need to do to get an ID. You might not be able to get one while you're inside, but knowing what you'll need to have when you're out will help you. If you're outside, contact your local Department of Motor Vehicles (DMV) office and find out what you need to get an ID before you wait in line. Ask for a form that lists the papers you need and ask for help if you need it.

List the items you need to get to obtain your ID and what actions you need to take to get those items:

_____

_____

8. Get Job Training or Employment Experience on the Inside

Learn what types of job training programs and trustee positions are available at your facility. If you have a trade you were practicing on the outside, see if you can apply it to work on the inside. Finding a way to be productive while on the inside will give you good things to talk about with your employer about your work history. It might take a while to get in a training program or become a trustee, but get on the list and be sure to follow all the rules in your inmate handbook. One rule violation could cost you this chance. Employers know all people make mistakes, but when they accept responsibility for their actions and make the most of their situation they show they can be good workers.

List chances for job training and actions you need to take to apply for them:

_____

_____

_____

9. Get Your Degree

If you didn't make it through high school and don't have your GED, work to earn it. If you're inside, sign up and take GED classes to prepare for the test. If you already have earned a high school diploma or GED, find out what other schooling is available to you. The farther you go in school, the better chance you'll have to land a good job.

List some actions you can take to further your education:

_____

_____

10. Keep Up with the Money You Owe

Find out how much you currently owe in fines, court costs, restitution and child support. Learn what options you have to set up payment plans so you can make it easier when you get out.

List the actions you will take to find out how much you owe and how you plan to pay what you owe upon release:

_____

_____

_____

11. Ask for Help

Reentry isn't always easy. It will take a lot of work. The good news is that many other dads—like you—have done it and made it. Even if this isn't the first time you have been released, the best path in life is to never come back. Work hard to succeed and when you need help, ask for it.

List the people that may be able to help you and the actions you will take to get their help:

_____

_____

_____

12. Find Support

You're not alone. There are groups in your community to help you. Find out who they are, where they are and what they do. Talk with your family, friends, counselors and parole or probation officers so they can refer you to helpful groups.

List the people and organizations that can help you as you prepare for your release and the actions you will take to get their support:

_____

_____

_____

13. Keep the Faith

Your faith community can provide a valuable source of support both while in prison and after release. Contact your facility's chaplain to learn what faith programs are offered. If you've made a faith commitment while in prison, maintain that connection while on the outside. Often faith-based organizations provide some of the best support for former prisoners.

List actions you will take to maintain your faith in your success:

_____

_____

_____

Session Log
Creating Your Reentry Plan

One new thing I learned today was_____

_____

_____

_____.

This information will help me become a better dad because_____

_____

_____

_____.

One way I will be a better dad is_____

_____

_____

_____.

Notes:

_____

_____

_____

_____

_____

_____

Reentry
Balancing Work and Family

"Imagine life as a game in which you are juggling five balls in the air. You name them —work, family, health, friends, and spirit— and you're keeping all of these in the air. You will soon understand that work is a rubber ball. If you drop it, it will bounce back. But the other four balls - family, health, friends, and spirit are made of glass. If you drop one of these, they will be scuffed, marked, nicked, damaged, or even shattered. They will never be the same. You must understand that and strive for balance in your life."
—Brian Dyson, CEO of Coca-Cola Enterprises from 1959-1994

When you are on the outside, the first thing you'll want to do is find a job and start a career. One of the biggest hurdles that dads face in being involved in their children's lives is to find a balance between work and family. Use the tips below to help you balance work and family once you get a job.

Tell Co-workers about Your Family Commitment
Talk with your friends and boss at work about your desire to balance work and family. This will help show them that you won't sacrifice family for your job.

Make Your Boss Your Ally
Working with your boss requires honesty, trust, and hard work. Work with your boss to create ways that help you meet your duty to both your job and family. One great way is to record your progress on the job in a weekly report to your boss. This way, you are judged on what you do and not just when you're present.

Stay Busy and Focused
Get your job done during the day so you can get home to your family. Close your office door, hang a "Do Not Disturb" sign on your cubicle or simply avoid office gossip. Let people know that you mean business when it comes to getting the job done. At the end of the day, you can relax knowing that you put in a full day of work.

Be a Team Player
Offer to help your co-workers and manager on special projects. It's a great way to prove that you can be flexible when needed. Treat people the way that you want to be treated, and they'll help you balance your work and family.

Be Choosy With Special Jobs
Think before you agree to overtime work or special jobs. It may be tempting to have the extra money or respect, but it may mean you'll have less time with your family.

Show Your Family Commitment
Display things like your children's artwork and family photos at the office so that everyone can see how committed you are to family. Also, keep a scheduled family commitment just like you keep a work commitment. People will quickly learn to respect both your time at work and with family.

Use Work Benefits that Help You Balance Work and Family
Your employer might offer benefits like flextime, shift swapping, telecommuting, paternity leave, or leave banks. Use them to help you with work and family time. If your employer doesn't have these benefits, talk with your human resources office about offering them.

Make Career Decisions as a Family

Try to find a job that limits stress when trying to balance work and family. As you consider new work or a promotion, compare the benefits of the job to how it will affect your family time.

Limit Work on Weekends, Vacations and Holidays

Don't make a habit of working on your days off. You need time away from work to focus on family time. Have a co-worker cover your work during a vacation. This will keep you from worrying about it while you're gone.

Be With Your Family Every Day

Spend time every day with your children and, if married, with your wife. Don't limit family time to the weekends. Find times and events that are just for family. Tuck your kids into bed, take an evening walk, or simply have dinner or breakfast together. This will help you stay connected to your family. If you don't live with your children, try to spend as much time with them as you can. Find ways to talk with them every day over the phone or by e-mail.

Create "Family Prime Time"

Create a daily block of time for family called "family prime time." Turn off your cell phone, laptop, and pager, and keep your work off-limits during this time.

Place Your Commitment in Writing

Create and sign a "family contract." Have your children and, if married, your wife sign it, too. Put in writing that you will balance success at work with success at home so that you can be an involved, responsible, and committed father. Read this contract at the start of every week to remind you of this commitment.

Session Log
Balancing Work and Family

One new thing I learned today was_____

_____

_____

_____.

This information will help me become a better dad because_____

_____

_____

_____.

One way I will be a better dad is_____

_____

_____

_____.

Notes:

_____

_____

_____

_____

_____

_____

APPENDIX:
Ages and Stages

First and Second Months

Physical Development	Motor Skills	Adaptive Development	Social Development
Average weight gain of about 5 to 7 ounces each week for the first 6 months. Height gain of approx. one inch each month Primarily breaths through nose	Typically unable to hold head up in first month, can turn head from side to side when lying on back, by second month will lift head. If held in a standing position, body will be limp at knees and hips. In supported position, back is rounded by second month, will try to hold head up but it will still bob forward. In first month, hands will usually be closed with grasp reflex strong, by second month hands frequently open and grasp, reflex fades.	Can fix eyes on moving object when held at a distance of 8–15 inches, by two months will follow toy from side to side. Prefers responsive human faces. Will quiet when hears your voice by two months, recognizes familiar voices. First month cries to show discomfort / distress.	Watches parent's face intently as he / she smiles at or plays with infant.

Parental Support and Encouragement

1. Holding, cuddling, rocking, talking and singing to your baby increases his (and your) sense of security.

2. Know that as you console and comfort your infant, he may not always be consolable regardless of what you do.

3. If your time together is limited, playing, talking and singing during his alert stages (dressing, bathing, feeding, walking, driving) is more fun for you both.

4. Start to establish bathing/feeding/bedtime routines and other habits to encourage predictable care patterns and discourage night awakening.

5. Stimulate your child by using age appropriate toys in your play interactions.

6. Discuss your questions about your baby's health and temperament with your healthcare professional, including how you are doing/feeling as this particular baby's father.

5.08_Appendix_Ages&Stages1

With Contributions from Dr. Kyle Pruett.

Third and Fourth Months

Physical Development	Motor Skills	Adaptive Development	Social Development
Increasing control of physical movements in neck, arms, legs and trunk. Soft spot on crown of head still open. (Careful!) Drooling begins.	Holds head more erect, more often. Can sit erect if propped up. Able to raise head and chest up, bears weight on forearms. Will briefly support some weight on legs if stood up. Inspects and plays with own hands. Can grasp and hold a rattle. Can bring objects to his mouth. (Careful!) Will clutch at blankets or clothes.	Locates sound by turning head and looking in same direction. Beginning hand-eye coordination. Starts to cry less often and cause is easier to discern. "Talks" a great deal when spoken to. Laughs, squeals, babbles, chuckles, and coos to show pleasure/excitement. Plays patty cake and peek-a-boo games.	Social smile begins to appear. Enjoy! Displays considerable interest in surroundings. Recognizes familiar faces and objects and shows pleasure. Seeks attention by vocalizing/moving/fussing, ceases to cry when familiar face enters the room. Begins to show memory of routines. Will turn away from over-stimulation and over-excitement

Parental Support and Encouragement

1. Continue to nurture your baby by holding, cuddling, rocking, etc.

2. Encourage baby's vocalization by talking and singing to him, mimicking the sounds he contributes to the "conversation".

3. Read and play simple games with your baby.

4. Help your baby learn self-consoling techniques by providing him with the same comfort object at bedtime or in new situations. He/she'll eventually choose one (blanket, stuffed animal, etc.). This encourages independence over time, not dependence.

5. Establish a bedtime routine and encourage your baby to console himself by putting him to bed awake after you have helped him quiet down.

6. Encourage play with age appropriate toys.

With Contributions from Dr. Kyle Pruett.

Fifth and Sixth Months

Physical Development	Motor Skills	Adaptive Development	Social Development
Birth weight has doubled. Growth rate slows. Baby may only gain 3 to 5 oz. and grow 1/2 inch each month for the next 6 months. Brain tissue still growing fast, but still fragile (still no shaking or roughhousing). Starts to get lower center teeth.	Able to sit for longer periods when back is well supported. Can bear most of weight when held (briefly) in standing position. Can roll from stomach to back. (Careful!) Puts feet to mouth. Sits in a high chair with back straight. Can grasp objects voluntarily. Takes objects directly to mouth. Holds bottle with both hands (briefly).	Looks for a dropped object, may initiate game. Able to sustain prolonged visual inspection of an object. Will turn head to side, and then look up or down. Squeals and coos in delight or excitement.	Smiles at own mirror image. Pats bottle or breast with both hands. Initiates more play. Holds up both arms to be picked up. Vocalizes displeasure when object/familiar person is taken away. Imitates (cough, tongue noises, etc.). Has frequent emotion changes.

Parental Support and Encouragement

1. Encourage your baby to talk by copying sounds she/he enjoys making.
2. Read to your baby and play music (of all kinds).
3. Play social games (patty cake, peek-a-boo, hide and seek with people/objects).
4. Establish limits on behavior (throwing) at this age, using distraction, stimulus control, structure and routine. Too early to establish discipline.
5. Keep up bathing/feeding/bedtime routine and other habits to discourage fatigue, disorganization and night awakening.
6. Encourage the baby to learn to console him/herself by putting him or her to bed awake.

With Contributions from Dr. Kyle Pruett.

Seventh and Eighth Months

Physical Development	Motor Skills	Adaptive Development	Social Development
Develops upper central teeth. Begins to show pattern in emptying bladder and bowel movements.	Sits, leaning forward on both hands. Bears full weight on feet in standing position, bounces actively. Transfers objects from one hand to the other. Bangs objects together. Rakes with fingers at small objects. Begins pinching grasp with fingers of smaller objects. Releases object at will (or not). Reaches for toys out of reach.	Responds to own name. Localizes sound by turning head and attending. Has beginning taste preferences. Produces vowel sounds and chain syllables (baba, dada, kiki) but does not know their meaning. Utterances, signal emphasis, preferences and emotion.	Is aware of non-family/familiar adults and increasingly aware of and possibly fearful of strangers. Imitates simple acts and noises. Can attract attention by coughing or snorting. Demonstrates dislike of food by keeping lips closed. Can exhibit aggressiveness/excitement by biting. Looks briefly for toy that disappears. Beginning response to word "no".

Parental Support and Encouragement

1. Encourage your baby to talk by talking to him, incorporating his new sounds in the "conversation".
2. Increase baby's social circle and involve baby in your social activities, with an eye on not too many strange handlers at once.
3. Read and sing to your baby and play music (of all kinds).
4. Play games (patty cake, peek-a-boo, tickle bee, etc).
5. Provide age appropriate toys.
6. Keep small objects out of reach.
7. To set limits for the infant at this age, use distraction, monitor stimulus amounts, structure, and routine.
8. Limit the number of rules but consistently enforce them.
9. Maintain the bedtime routine. Encourage the baby to learn to console him/herself by putting him/her to bed awake.

With Contributions from Dr. Kyle Pruett.

Ninth and Tenth Months

Physical Development	Motor Skills	Adaptive Development	Social Development
More teeth erupt. (Distressing) Infant is able to raise head while lying down or in a sitting position.	Starts to crawl, may progress backward at first, by 10th month will be pulling self forward. (Careful!) Can change from lying position to sitting position. Sits steadily on floor for longer periods. Pulls up and stands holding onto furniture. Uses thumb and index finger in crude pincher grasp of small objects. Dominant hand use can start to appear.	Depth perception is increasing. Turns head directly toward sound. Responds to simple commands. Says "dada" and "mama" with beginning meaning. Imitates definite speech sounds. Speaks gibberish (sounds like a sentence but isn't yet).	Parents increasingly important as play and comfort partners. Increased interest in pleasing parent. May show fear of going to bed or being left alone. Puts arm in front of face to avoid washing. Imitates expressions. Likes attention; will repeat action or pull at your clothes to attract attention. Cries when scolded/scared. Demonstrates beginning independence in dressing, feeding and testing parents.

Parental Support and Encouragement

1. Your baby is in motion, so make sure your home is baby proof to prevent unnecessary accidents.

2. Provide an area where baby can explore and practice new skills.

3. Talk with your baby, respond to his/her vocal efforts.

4. Read to and sing to your baby and play music (of all kinds).

5. Play social games (patty cake, peek-a-boo, etc.).

6. Provide age appropriate toys.

7. To set limits on physical aggression and discipline with the infant at this age, use distraction, monitor stimulus load, structure, and routine.

8. Limit the number of rules but consistently enforce them.

9. Maintain an established bedtime routine.

With Contributions from Dr. Kyle Pruett.

Eleventh and Twelfth Months

Physical Development	Motor Skills	Adaptive Development	Social Development
More teeth grow in. Birth weight has probably tripled and height has doubled since birth. Soft spot on head is almost closed.	Crawls well. Walks holding onto furniture or your hand. Can sit down from standing position. When sitting, pivots to reach toward back to pick up an object. Holds a crayon. Explores objects more thoroughly. (Still uses mouth—careful!) Drops objects into a container (any container). Can turn pages in a book, usually many at a time	Can follow rapidly moving objects. Comprehends hundreds of words although toddlers may only speak two or three words. Recognizes objects by name. Understands simple one stage commands.	Experiences joy/esteem when a task is mastered. Reacts to restrictions with frustration. Shows emotions of all kinds. Fearful in strange situations. May further develop habits with comfort objects — "security blanket".

Parental Support and Encouragement

1. Praise toddler for good behavior, but don't overdo.
2. Encourage language development by reading books to the toddler, singing, talking about what you are doing and seeing. Allow him some cardboard books to turn pages by 'self'.
3. Encourage (SAFE) exploration and initiative.
4. Encourage the toddler to play alone (he'll need some structure/check-in time) as well as with playmates, siblings and parents.
5. To set limits for a toddler, use distraction, gentle restraint, removal of object from toddler or, if you believe in it and can do it calmly, time out.
6. Limit number of rules and avoid unnecessary conflict situations by heading off trouble before it starts. Structure really helps.
7. Maintain a regular bedtime. Will make it through some nights completely.
8. Discuss toilet training with your healthcare professional.
9. TV still has nothing much to offer infants compared with human interaction.

With Contributions from Dr. Kyle Pruett.

First and Second Years

Physical Development	Motor Skills	Adaptive Development	Social Development
The usual weight gain in this period is 4 to 6 pounds. Average growth is 4 to 5 inches. May have daytime bowel control.	Walks without help. Is very mobile, will start to climb stairs, at first by creeping and then with two feet on each step. Will learn to run, at first falling often. As he/she gains more balance, he assumes standing position without help. Will learn to stop suddenly without falling, can pick up objects and kick and throw a ball. Toddler likes to push and pull toys. Seats self in chair. Uses a cup. Scribbles spontaneously. Can build tower of 6 or 7 blocks. Can turn doorknob and unscrew lids.	Able to identify some shapes. Displays intense interest in pictures. Will develop a spoken vocabulary during this period of around 300 words. Understands 1 or 2 directional commands. Refers to self by name. Often talks incessantly.	Tolerates some separation from parent. Expresses emotions, hugs and kisses parents and has temper tantrums. Open drawers and doors to find objects. Is a great imitator. Beginning awareness of ownership. Has some sense of time; waits in response to "just a minute". Dresses self in simple clothes.

Parental Support and Encouragement

1. Praise toddler for good behavior, but don't overdo.
2. Encourage language development by reading books, singing, talking about what you are doing and seeing.
3. Reinforce self-care and self-expression.
4. To promote a sense of competence and control, invite the toddler to make simple choices whenever possible.
5. Encourage the toddler to be assertive in appropriate situations.
6. Decide what limits are important to you and your toddler. Briefly tell your toddler why she is being disciplined. Attempt to be as consistent as possible when enforcing limits. Keep it short and sweet.
7. When disciplining, make a verbal separation between him/her and his/her behavior: "I love you, but I don't like it when you…"
8. When possible, give a toddler a "yes" as well as a "no" (you can not play with the vase, you can play with the blocks).

—continued

With Contributions from Dr. Kyle Pruett.

First and Second Year Parental Support and Encouragement —continued

9. Do not get into a power struggle with your child. Sidestep conflict and assert your power calmly and swiftly. You can control only your own responses to the toddler's behavior. For example, you cannot make a toddler sleep. But you can insist she stay in his/her room.

10. Recognize that toilet training is part of a developmentally appropriate learning. Delay training until the toddler is dry for periods of about two hours, knows the difference between wet and dry, can pull his pants up, wants to learn and gives a signal when he is about to have a bowel movement.

11. Spend individual time with the child, playing with him, hugging or holding him, taking walks, painting, and doing puzzles together.

12. Appreciate the child's investigative nature, and do not excessively limit this.

13. Promote physical activity in a safe environment.

14. Encourage parallel play with other children; do not expect shared play yet.

15. Use time out or remove source of conflict for unacceptable behavior.

16. Prepare strategies to deal with night awakening, night fears, nightmares, and night terrors.

With Contributions from Dr. Kyle Pruett.

Third Year

Physical Development	Motor Skills	Adaptive Development	Social Development
Usually will have gained 4 to 6 pounds and grow approx. 3 inches. Will occasionally have night time control of bowel and bladder.	Rides tricycle. Jumps off bottom stair. Stands on one foot. Goes up stairs alternating feet. Tries to dance. Can draw circles and crosses. Builds towers and bridges with blocks.	Has a spoken vocabulary of about 900 words. Uses complete sentences with three or four words. May talk constantly. Dresses self almost completely. Feeds self. Can help with small one or two staged tasks. May have fear of dark or going to bed. Begins to work out social interaction though play. Talks to dolls, animals, trucks, etc. More able to share, wait turn.	Is still self-centered in thought and behavior. Has beginning ability to view concepts from another's perspective. Usually attempts to please parents and conform to their expectations. Is aware of family relationships and sex roles. Boys usually identify with father, family males and girls with mother, family females.

Parental Support and Encouragement

1. Praise the child for good behavior and accomplishment.
2. Encourage the child to talk with you about his/her preschool, friends, and observations. Can answer simple, non-judgmental questions.
3. Encourage interactive reading with the child. Be patient—they adore repetition often beyond adult tolerance.
4. Spend individual time with the child whenever possible.
5. Provide opportunities for the three-year-old to socialize with other children.
6. Recognize that toilet training is part of a developmentally appropriate learning. Delay toilet training until the toddler is dry for periods of about two hours, knows the difference between wet and dry, can pull his pants up, wants to learn and gives a signal when he is about to have a bowel movement.
7. Promote physical activity and play.
8. Reinforce limits and appropriate behavior.
9. Give child opportunities to make choices.
10. Limit TV to an average of an hour a day of appropriate, educational, non-adult programming. Watch with them.

With Contributions from Dr. Kyle Pruett.

Fourth Year

Physical Development	Motor Skills	Adaptive Development	Social Development
Usually will have gained 4 to 6 pounds and grow approx. 3 inches.	Skips and hops on one foot. Catches and throws a ball. Uses scissors successfully. Can draw squares and stick figures.	Has a vocabulary of about 1500 words. Uses complete sentences with three or four words. Talks constantly. Questioning is at its peak. Tells exaggerated stories. Knows simple songs. Understands "under", "on top of", "beside", "in back" or "in front of". Repeats four digits. Often loves to help cook, clean, put laundry away.	Quite independent. Tends still to be selfish, impatient, and aggressive. Boasts tattles and tells family tales with little restraint. Still has many fears. (thunder, dogs) Imaginary friends are common. Works through unresolved conflict (with help). Understands time better, especially in terms of sequence of daily events. May count but has poor math concepts. Takes aggression and frustration out on parents and siblings. Do's and don'ts become important.

Parental Support and Encouragement

1. Praise the child for good behavior and accomplishment, but don't exaggerate-the outside world won't.
2. Encourage the child to talk with you about his/her preschool, friends, observations—the good and the less good. Answer questions.
3. Encourage interactive reading with the child.
4. Spend individual time with the child whenever possible.
5. Provide opportunities for socialization with other children.
6. Promote physical activity of all kinds.
7. Reinforce limits and appropriate behavior.
8. Give child opportunities to make choices, be creative, participate in generous and giving acts in family and neighborhood.
9. Limit TV to an average of an hour a day of appropriate, educational, non-adult programming. Watch with them!
10. Encourage assertiveness without aggression.
11. Enlarge the child's experiences.

With Contributions from Dr. Kyle Pruett.

Fifth Year

Physical Development	Motor Skills	Adaptive Development	Social Development
May begin getting permanent teeth. Have usually established hand preference.	Skips and hops on alternate feet. Catches and throws a ball. Jumps ropes and skates. Ties shoes. Prints a few letters, numbers and words.	Has a vocabulary of about 2500 words. Uses complete sentences. Names coins, colors, days of week, months. Asks meaning of words. Asks inquisitive questions. Can do all self care.	Is more settled and eager to get down to business. Is independent and more trustworthy. Relies on outer authority to control their world. Likes rules and tries to play by them but may cheat to avoid losing. Begins to notice the outside world and is curious to where/how he belongs. Enjoys doing activities with parent of same sex.

Parental Support and Encouragement

1. Praise the child for cooperation and accomplishment.
2. Encourage the child to talk with you about his/her school or friends. May help to prime the pump by telling him/her a little about yours.
3. Encourage the child to express his/her feelings.
4. Encourage interactive reading with the child. Daily.
5. Spend individual time with the child doing something you both enjoy.
6. Enhance the child's breadth of experience. Take on something new to BOTH of you.
7. Provide opportunities to interact with other children.
8. Help the child learn to get along with peers. Set appropriate examples in your own social behavior.
9. Promote physical activities of all kinds, continue to limit TV.
10. Expect the child to follow family rules, such as those for bedtime, TV, and chores.
11. Teach the child the difference between right and wrong, respect for authority, anger management.
12. Assign age appropriate chores.
13. Introduce to computer use at home or library.

With Contributions from Dr. Kyle Pruett.

Sixth and Seventh Years

Physical Development	Motor Skills	Adaptive Development	Social Development
Height and weight gain slow, average growth 2 inches and 5 pounds.	Enjoys practicing new language, memory and math skills.	At table, uses knife to spread butter or jam.	Can share and cooperate better.
Wisdom teeth begin.	Counts 13 pennies.	At play, cuts, folds, pastes paper.	Has strong need for play with peers.
Gradual increase in activity to constant.	Knows whether it is morning or afternoon.	Enjoys making simple figures in clay or play dough.	Often engages in rough play.
Still uses fingers when eating.	Defines common objects such as "fork" and "chair" in terms of use.	Takes a bath without supervision, performs bedtime activities alone.	Is often jealous of younger brother and sister.
Loves to practice new physical skills.	Obeys triplet commands in succession.	Likes table games, checkers, and simple card games.	Does what he/she sees adults doing good or bad.
Likes to draw, print and color.	Says which is pretty and which is ugly when looking at pictures.	Influenced by school friends.	Often has frustration.
	Reads from memory, enjoys oral spelling games.	Has own way of doing things.	Likes to boast.
	Likes to boast.	Tries out own abilities.	Will cheat to win.
			Has difficulty owning up to misdeeds.
			Sometimes steals money or attractive items and then lies.

Parental Support and Encouragement

1. Praise your child for cooperation and accomplishments.
2. Encourage your child to talk about school, friends or observations by listening carefully and remembering what they say. Answer their questions.
3. Encourage your child to express his or her feelings, and help by appropriately expressing yours.
4. Encourage reading - both alone and together.
5. Spend individual time with your child, something both of you enjoy.
6. Enlarge your child's experiences through family trips and outings.
7. Help your child to learn how to get along with peers.
8. Help your child learn how to follow group rules.
9. Promote daily physical activity in a safe environment and monitor TV habits.
10. Set limits and establish consequences for misbehavior.
11. Encourage self-discipline and impulse control.
12. Expect your child to follow family rules, such as those at bedtime, television viewing and chores.
13. Teach your child to respect authority by being a respectful authority.
14. Foster your child's ability to communicate with you, teachers and other adults by going to school.
15. Make sure your child understands the difference between right and wrong.
16. Teach your child how to manage anger and resolve conflicts without physical or emotional violence.

With Contributions from Dr. Kyle Pruett.

Eighth and Ninth Years

Physical Development	Motor Skills	Adaptive Development	Social Development
Continues to grow 2 inches and gain about 6 pounds a year.	Attends third and fourth grade.	Makes use of common tools such as hammer, saw, house-hold utensils.	Easy to get along with at home; better behaved.
Always on the go: jumps, chases and skips.	Gives similarities and differences between two things from memory.	Helps with household tasks.	Likes the reward system.
Increased smoothness and speed in the motor control.	Repeats days of the week and months in order.	Looks after all of own needs at table.	Dramatizes often.
Movement fluid; often graceful and poised.	Counts backward from 20.	Exercises some choice in making purchases.	Is more sociable.
Dresses self completely with predictable personal style.	Makes change out of a quarter.	Goes about community freely.	Is better 'behaved' by adult standards.
Eyes and hands are well coordinated.	Reads classic books and enjoys comics.	Great reader likes pictorial magazines.	Interested in boy-girl relationships but will not admit it.
	Is more aware of time; can be relied on to get to school on time.	Enjoys school.	Likes to compete & play games.
	Is afraid of failing a grade; ashamed of bad grades, mistakes.	Likely to overdo; hard to quiet down after recess.	Is more critical of self.
			Has developed a personal style.
			Knows right from wrong and can dispense crude justice.

Parental Support and Encouragement

1. Serve as a positive ethical, moral and behavioral role model.
2. Contribute to the child's self-esteem by honoring his/her effort and showing affection.
3. Show interest in the child's school performance and activities by visiting school and being aware of projects. Display work at home.
4. Set reasonable but challenging expectations.
5. Promote self-responsibility.
6. Show affection and respect in the family.
7. Spend some individual time with each child.
8. Participate in games and physical activities with the child.
9. Encourage positive interactions between the child, parents and siblings.
10. Share meals as a family whenever possible, and encourage child to help in preparation.
11. Know the child's friends and their families.
12. Handle anger constructively in the family.
13. Spend time talking to each other.
14. Teach your child how to manage anger and resolve conflicts without physical or emotional violence.

With Contributions from Dr. Kyle Pruett.

Tenth Through Eleventh Years

Physical Development	Motor Skills	Adaptive Development	Social Development
Slow growth in height and rapid weight gain, may become obese during this period if passive. Posture is more similar to an adult's. Pubescent changes may begin to appear, especially in females as body lines soften and round out. Rest of teeth will erupt and tend toward full development.	Attend fifth and sixth grades. Writes occasional short letters to friends or relative on own initiative. Uses phone/computer for practical purposes. Responds to magazines, TV or other advertising by mailing coupons. Reads for practical information or own enjoyment.	Does occasional or brief work on own initiative around home and neighborhood. Is sometimes left alone at home for short periods of time. Is successful in looking after own needs or those of other children left in care briefly. Cooks and sews in small way. Does easy repair. Cares for pets. Writes brief stories, simple paintings or drawings. Washes and dries own hair but may need reminding to do so.	Likes family; family really has meaning. Likes mother and wants to please her. Demonstrates affection. Dad is adored and idolized. (Enjoy it while it lasts!) Loves friends, talks about them constantly. Chooses friends more selectively. Beginning to take an interest in the opposite sex. Is more diplomatic. Can discuss moral choices when facing right vs. wrong decisions.

Parental Support and Encouragement

1. Anticipate wide range of pre-adolescent behaviors including the strong influence of peers, a change in the communication pattern between adolescents and parents, new challenges to parental authority, conflicts over independence, refusal to participate in some family activities, moodiness, and new risk taking.
2. Serve as a positive ethical and behavioral role model.
3. Contribute to the child's self-esteem by praising him and showing affection toward him and within the family. (see above)
4. Show interest in the child's school performance/activities. Know teachers and major events. Set reasonable but challenging expectations.
5. Promote self-responsibility at and away from home.
6. Participate in games and physical activities with the child.
7. Share meals as a family whenever possible. Leave the stress at work.
8. Foster conversation and open communication in the family.
9. Know the child's friends and their families.
10. Encourage the development of good sibling relationships.
11. Discuss (and demonstrate) value/meaning of money in family and society. Discuss allowance, chores, savings, gift giving, charity, etc.
12. Teach your child how to manage anger and resolve conflicts without physical or emotional violence.

With Contributions from Dr. Kyle Pruett.

Twelfth Through Fourteenth Years

Physical Development	Intellectual Development	Relationship Skills
Maximum growth increases, especially in height. Gain in height is abrupt at the onset and continues at a rapid rate the first 2 years, followed by a deceleration.	Exploring limited ability to think abstractly about culture, politics, religion, permanence of death.	Often indecisive.
Acne probable.	Tries out various roles, identities.	Has wide mood swings, frustrates them and you.
Girls are generally 2 years ahead of boys in development at first.	Conforms to group norms of dress, activities and vocabulary while seeking 'individuality'.	Daydreams intensely.
Beginning of menstruation (avg., age 12 1/2 yr., range 11-16).	Measures attractiveness by acceptance or rejection of peers.	Expresses anger outwardly with moodiness, temper outburst, verbal insults and name-calling.
Boys experience nocturnal emissions.	Develops close idealized friendships with members of the same sex.	Attempts repeated separation from parents and concentrates on relationships with peers.
Coordination improves until approximately 14 when it reaches a plateau and the child may then appear awkward, especially boys.	Differences are intolerable to the peer group; uniformity is the norm.	Is period of highest parent-child conflict.
Has general anxiety about appearance and an intense pre-occupation with developing body size.	Struggle for mastery takes place within peer group.	Takes instant exception to opinion expressed by others.
Anxiety about functioning well in society and especially about being small.	Effectively uses humor to criticize family and friends.	Forms ego ideal of male through relationships with father.
Struggles to master new physical capabilities.	Watching TV, listening to music, talking on the phone/ internet, sports and group activities are favorite past-times.	Has strong desire to remain dependent on parents while trying to detach.
Is very self-centered.	Boys interest center around sports, sports figures and video games.	Craves privacy.
Compares "normality" with peers of same sex.	Girls discuss boys, clothes, and makeup.	

Parental Support and Encouragement

1. Understand that the adolescent may be unwilling to participate in some family activities and may suddenly challenge parental authority.

2. Decide with the adolescent when he/she can do things on their own, including staying at home alone.

3. Establish realistic expectations for family rules, with increasing independence and responsibility given to the adolescent who has shown he/she can handle increasing doses of it.

— continued

With Contributions from Dr. Kyle Pruett.

Twelfth Through Fourteenth Years Parental Support and Encouragement — continued

4. Establish and communicate clear limits and consequences for breaking rules. Consciously use humor whenever possible.

5. Emphasize the importance of school academically and socially.

6. Enhance the adolescent's self-esteem by providing praise, reassurance and minimize criticism, nagging, sarcasm and belittling comments (and you WILL be tempted!).

7 Spend time with the adolescent, even if they don't ask for it.

8. Respect the adolescent's need for privacy both physical and emotional.

9. Discuss with child your expectations about drugs, alcohol, and respectful intimate relationships now and down the road.

10. Teach your child how to manage anger and resolve conflicts without physical or emotional violence.

With Contributions from Dr. Kyle Pruett.

Fifteenth Through Seventeenth Years

Physical Development	Intellectual Development	Relationship Skills
Female attains physical maturity. Possible/probable sexual/drug/alcohol experimentation with peers and confusion over roles are possible. Masturbation is a central activity or concern, depending on individual.	Abstract thinking established. Has ability to think logically and maintain an argument. Gradually realizes that others' thoughts are not directed toward them. Worries about school work. Enjoys intellectual powers. Invest love in another, may experience the intensity of "being in love." Acceptance by peers is extremely important—fear of rejection continues. Peer group sets behavioral standards. Explores "sex appeal" power. Turns toward heterosexuality (if homosexual, may know by this time). Sports activities are important. Feels need for a car for autonomy. Has or wants outside jobs to earn money.	Is very self-centered, increased arrogance. Tends toward inner experience and self-discovery. Struggles to define attractiveness as perceived through personal appearance. Tends to withdraw when upset or hurt. Feelings of inadequacy are common; has difficulty asking for help. Low points in parent-child relationship recur, emotional detachment frequent. Greatest push for independence, causing major conflicts over independence.

Parental Support and Encouragement

1. Decide with the adolescent when she can do things on his/her own, including staying at home alone.
2. Establish realistic expectations for family rules, with increasing independence and responsibility given to the adolescent.
3. Establish and communicate clear limits and reach an agreement on appropriate consequences for breaking rules.
4. Continue to stress the importance of school, reinforcing your expectations regarding their future successes.
5. Enhance the adolescent's self-esteem by providing praise and minimize criticism, nagging and belittling comments. (see above)
6. Spend time with the adolescent. (see above)
7. Respect the adolescent's need for privacy. (see above)
8. Refresh the previous discussion about drugs, alcohol and sex, no matter how uncomfortable. Pediatricians/nurses can help with suggestions. Talk IS the anti-drug.
9. Teach your child how to manage anger and resolve conflicts without physical or emotional violence.

With Contributions from Dr. Kyle Pruett.

Eighteenth Year and Up

Physical Development	Intellectual Development	Relationship Skills
Attains physical maturity in male; growth in height ceases at 18 to 20 years.	Is capable of protecting their identity in face of diversity.	Has a more stable, predictable emotion.
More comfortable with physical growth andattractiveness.	Able to view complex problems more objectively, less personally.	Anger is more apt to be concealed.
Sexual identity is generally secured.	Able to make stable relationships and form attachments to another.	Is in phase of consolidation of identity.
Body image and gender role definition are nearly selected.	Importance of peer groups is lessening.	Stability of self-esteem occurs.
	New depths in interpersonal relationships form.	Begins to think of the possibility of more permanent male-female relationship.
	Social roles are defined and expressed.	Have fewer conflicts with family.
	Creative imagination cools.	Is independent from family.
	Prefers purposeful action.	Is able to take or leave advice.
	Life goals and tasks are taking shape.	
	Pursues a career or vocation and decisions about lifestyle.	
	Is at a decisive turning point.	
	Defines purpose in terms of life goals.	
	Relationships with opposite sex are less self-centered.	

Parental Support and Encouragement

1. Encourage the older adolescent's independent decision making when appropriate.
2. Discuss his or her plans for independent living/college/job, financial realities.
3. Establish joint expectations with the adolescent regarding family rules and responsibilities.
4. Enhance the adolescent's self esteem by providing praise and recognizing positive behavior and achievements.
5. Minimize criticism, nagging, and derogatory comments.
6. Spend time with teen.
7. Respect the adolescence's need for privacy. (see above)
8. Teach your child how to manage anger and resolve conflicts without physical or emotional violence.

With Contributions from Dr. Kyle Pruett.